Christ &
Culture

INVITED TO GO & TEACH

Student Workbook

WHEATON PRESS
READ. RESPOND. REFLECT.

Culture & Theology
Student Workbook

ISBN-13:978-0692385012
ISBN-10: 0692385010

1. Christian Education – Discipleship 2. Spiritual Formation – Discipleship. 3. Culture & Theology – Education. 4. Nonfiction-Religion and Spirituality-Christian Life. 5. Nonfiction-Spiritual Growth-Christ-centered.

Contact the publisher for discounted copies for partner schools and receive free resources and training for teachers.

Learn more at WheatonPress.com or email WheatonPress@gmail.com

To those who will live out the mission of reflecting Christ in their circles of influence.

But you will be my
WITNESSES
...to the ends of the earth.

Acts 1:8

Christ & Culture
INVITED TO GO & TEACH

Equipping Students to Reflect Christ

	STEP ONE	STEP TWO	STEP THREE	STEP FOUR
Growth Emphasis	An Emphasis on Believing	An Emphasis on Following	An Emphasis on Loving	An Emphasis on Going
Essential Questions	1. What does a healthy, mature follower of Christ believe? 2. How does a healthy, mature follower of Christ live?	3. How do I grow as a healthy, mature follower of Christ? 4. How do I equip others to grow as healthy, mature followers of Christ?	5. Who do others say Jesus is? 6. Who do I say Jesus is?	7. What do I believe? 8. Why do I believe? 9. How will I communicate to others?
Essential Outcomes	Understand and articulate Christ-centered beliefs	Develop authentic Christ-centered values	Develop and articulate a Christ-centered vision	Develop a clear Christ-centered personal mission
Courses	Foundations of Faith	Spiritual Formations Leadership, Evangelism, & Discipleship	Life of Christ Philosophy & Theology	Doctrine & Apologetics Christ & Culture
Leadership Pipeline	D Groups	Mentor Project	LEAD U	LAUNCH The Poiema Project

Breakfast on the Beach
John 21

A simple approach to Christ & Culture

Just as there exists an infinite list of different ways that contemporary culture is in tension or conflict with Christ, there are also numerous ways that Christians have attempted to adopt or adapt to cultural norms or trends. Some ways have bolstered while others have hindered the advance or cause of Christ.

As a result, a conventional approach to a Christ and culture class would be to list off modern cultural issues and then attempt to find or discover verses that apply to various sides of the cultural issue.

For the purposes of this course, we will take a different approach. Rather than start with a cultural issue and then seek to discover relevant references that may or may be made out of context to create a lesson plan this course will attempt to start with Scripture and then identify the cultural issues that are addressed within.

The historical book of Acts and Paul's letter to the Romans will act as our primary guide to accomplish these purposes. Through the page of Acts, Paul's personal physician Luke provides an eyewitness account to the cultural war and transformation that occurred when a small group of Jewish disciples carried the counter-cultural message of the resurrection of their rabbi to the world.

The story begins in the synagogues of Jewish Jerusalem and is carried across the seas to Greece, Asia, and Rome. Along the way, the disciples face personal, cultural conflicts as they are forced to identify and differentiate their new understanding from their former way of life to determine what was cultural and what was Theological?

Throughout the narrative of Acts, we watch as the Gospel is communicated with abandonment and without shame in a perverse world run by the accepted cultural norms of monism, materialism, and idealism.

Then in Paul's treatise of the Gospel to the Romans, we read of other cultural conflicts between the Theology of Christ-centered Theism and the accepted worldviews that still contaminated the young believers at the time. Issues of creation, sexuality, gender, prejudice, and racism, the purpose of the church and the relationship between the church and the government (particularly one that was obscenely corrupt) as well as personal and corporate leadership issues are all addressed in the letter.

We live in a culture where within a few months you will leave the safe confines of your Christian school education, and you will become one of the mere handful within your generation who will be entrusted, much like the disciples in their day, with the fulfillment of God's mission for the world in your generation.

How did a handful of Christ followers respond to the invitation of Jesus to pick up His co-mission and under the power of the Holy Spirit multiply the glory of God to the ends of the earth?

If you have ever wondered or pondered that question, then this course is for you.

It is designed as the culmination of your study and as your final preparation to encourage, equip and envision you for your next steps in your unique role in the mission and purpose of God in your generation.

Hopefully, by now you know that the purpose of this four-year scope and sequence has never been to simply encourage students to hold onto their faith, but to equip you to give it away.

Through the book of Acts and the letter to the Romans, our goal is to give you one last opportunity to learn and grow together with the community of believers in your class before you are each intentionally sent out envisioned and equipped to accomplish that goal.

Blessings on you as you study, prepare and grow this semester.

Class Overview

Essential Questions

1 How will I communicate what I believe in the context of my culture?

2 How will I reflect what I believe in my circles of influence beyond the walls?

Unit Essential Questions

1 What would it take for God to accomplish His mission in and through my life?

2 How do I make sense of my disintegrated culture?

3 How did the early church fulfill the mission of God?

4 What are some of the challenges and opportunities in my generation?

5 How will I respond and effectively reflect Christ's mission in my generation?

Course Description

This class will challenge students with the eternal plan and purpose of God for the earth and their role in fulfilling His mission. Students to build a solid theological foundation for the biblical history of the cultural interaction and response to the plan of God; examine key New Testament interactions in the early church to identify early conflicts and victories; examine key historical witnesses and events up to the modern day challenges faced by this generation.

Finally students will be challenged to reflect on God's plan for integration and develop a personal plan for responding to the invitation to participate in the mission of God beyond the walls of their classroom and to reflect Christ in their circles of influence.

Learning Outcomes

A Identify the tension between the eternal plan of God and the reality of operating in a disintegrated culture.

B Examine Scripture to identify major themes and cultural responses in the interaction between God, His people and those who oppose His mission.

C Survey major historical events and figures that impacted culture during their generation and beyond in order to build a context for understanding current cultural challenges and option for taking the next step toward fulfilling the mission of God.

D What are some of the modern cultural challenges, tensions and opportunities faced by by generation from the perspective of God's eternal plan?

E How do I experience integration in my life as I look beyond the classroom and discover the circles of influence that God is trusting me with?

F How will I respond and reflect Christ in my generation?

Unit 1   Understanding the tension between Christ & Culture

1   What is the learning goal for Christ & Culture?

2   What happens when 8th grade boys pray?

3   What would it take for God to accomplish His mission in our culture?

4   Why is it so difficult?
        What will we commit to ourselves and each other?

5   How do we apply Christ's invitation to breakfast on the beach to our lives?

6   Who will we become?

7   How do I make sense of Culture?
        Why is culture disintegrated?

8   What is the impact of disintegration on our culture?

9   How do we reintegrate culture to reflect it's intended purpose?

Unit 2   Acts: Invited to co-mission with the Messiah

Unit 3   Our Great Cloud of Witnesses Projects

Unit 4   From Conversation to Crossing Cultures Leadership Project

Unit 5   Crossing Cultures: The Journey

          • Crossing Cultures: the first missionary journey
          • Crossing Cultures: the second missionary journey
          • Crossing Cultures: the third missionary journey
          • Crossing Cultures: the journey to Rome

Unit 6   Romans
Unit 7   Circles of influence

How will I be graded?
Socratic rubric

Standard	Element not present for assessment	Does not meet standard	Meets standard at basic level	Above average in standard	Proficient in standard
	1	2	3	4	5
Conduct	Arrives unprepared without notes, pencil/pen, or perhaps even without the text.	Displays little respect for the learning process. Argumentative or apathetic. Takes advantage of minor distractions. Uses inappropriate language. Speaks to individuals rather than ideas. Arrives unprepared without notes, pencil/pen, or perhaps even without the text.	Participates and expresses a belief that his/her ideas are important in understanding the text. May make insightful comments, but does not contribute to the progress of the conversation.	Generally shows composure, but may display impatience with contradictory or confusing ideas. Comments, but does not necessarily encourage others to participate.	Demonstrates respect for the learning process. Has patience with different opinions and complexity of ideas. Shows initiative by asking others for clarification. Brings others into the conversation. Moves the conversation forward. Speaks to all of the participants. Avoids talking too much.
Speaking and reasoning	Arrives unprepared without notes, pencil/pen, or perhaps even without the text.	Extremely reluctant to participate even when called upon. Comments are illogical and meaningless. May mumble or express incomplete ideas. Little or no account taken of previous comments or important ideas in the text.	Responds to questions but may have to be called upon by others. Has read the text but not put much effort into preparing questions and ideas for the seminar. Comments take details into account but may not flow logically in conversation.	Responds to questions voluntarily. Comments show an appreciation for the text. Comments are logical, but not connected to other speakers. Ideas interesting enough that others respond.	Understands questions asked before answering them. Cites evidence from text. Expresses thoughts in complete sentences. Moves conversation forward. Makes connections between ideas.
Listening	Arrives unprepared without notes, pencil/pen, or perhaps even without the text.	Appears uninvolved in the seminar. Comments display complete misinterpretation of questions or comments of other participants.	Appears to find some ideas unimportant while responding to others. May require questions or confusions to be repeated due to inattention. Takes few notes during the seminar in response to ideas and comments.	Generally pays attention and responds thoughtfully to ideas and questions of other participants and the leader. Absorption in own ideas may distract the participant from the ideas of others.	Pays attention to details. Writes down questions. Responses take into account all participants. Demonstrates that he/she has kept up. Points out faulty logic respectfully. Overcomes distractions.
Critical reading	Arrives unprepared without notes, pencil/pen, or perhaps even without the text.	Student is unprepared for the seminar. Important words, phrases, and/or ideas in the text are unfamiliar. No notes or questions are marked in the text. No attempt made to get help with difficult material.	Appears to have read or skimmed the text, but has not marked the text or made meaningful notes or questions. Little evidence of serious reflection prior to the seminar.	Has read the text and comes with some ideas from it, but these may not be written out in advance. Occasionally references terms and page numbers.	Thoroughly familiar with the text. Has notations and questions in the margins (when applicable). Key words, phrases, and ideas are highlighted. Possible contradictions are identified. Uses terms and page numbers where appropriate.

Understanding the tension between Christ & Culture

Christ & Culture

My Expectations

1   The name I like to be called is (nickname) _____.

2   The reason I'm taking this class (other than "because it's required") is:

3   One thing I'm looking forward to in this class is:

4   Two things I want to learn in this class include:

1)

2)

5   One goal I have for myself this year is:

6   One thing my teacher could pray for me about this semester would be:

7   My relationship with Jesus up to this point in my life could best be described as:

What happens when 8th grade boys pray?
What would it take?

Many years ago, I had the privilege of being a student ministry Pastor at a church that experienced a revival among the students.

Students whose hearts had been hardened toward God and the things of God experienced a radical softening and hunger to live Christ-centered lives focused on reflecting Christ in their circles of influence. Students continuously prayed with and for each other and lives were increasingly transformed over the course of time.

Other students who were far from God heard about a place where their peers would pray vulnerable prayers to a God who would listen to their cries, and they accepted invitations to come and check things out for themselves.

Still other students who were familiar with the God of the Bible and were frustrated with their own experience of cultural Christianity began to hear about what God was doing, and they started to ask if they could come and check things out for themselves.

During that season the "formula" for conventional student ministry was tossed aside as each time that students gathered they were desperately waiting on God to hear and answer their prayers for life change in themselves and others.

It was not uncommon during that season for new students to walk into student-led prayer meetings and ask, "Is this the place where people pray for you?" and then have them unload either a list of hurts, habits, and hang-ups a mile long or sometimes just one burden that had been weighing them down.

As student ministry leaders our job was mostly to try to stay out of God's way.

There was not really a time for strategizing or planning out a given night because even during the times that we would attempt to assemble even the most basic of outlines things would happen where we would recognize our need to step back and allow for God to move.

There had already been a brief time of prayer to open the evening, and there had been so much happening in and through the lives of students throughout the week that it was difficult to stay up to date on what God was doing. One evening students were gathered in a large circle inside our cramped youth room I felt led by the Spirit of God to ask students to share updates so that we could rejoice with or pray for each other.

A couple of 8th-grade boys began by sharing what God had been doing in their middle school. The previous week students had participated in a "See You At The Pole" event but had been discouraged by the overall turnout of students from their school. They had felt that in middle school their size that it was disheartening that so few students had attended. Basically, it was this small group of 8th-grade boys, and a 6th grader nicked named "Mikey."

As they prayed together that morning, they felt the Spirit of God compelling them to continue the process of praying for their peers and for their school. So they devised a concept that they termed "the 30-second drop."

The idea of the 30-second drop was that when they would arrive at their locker in the morning to grab their books before their first class, they would individually drop to one knee in front of their locker and pray that the students whose lockers were on either side of them would have their lives changed by Jesus.

As these students told their story, they became more and more excited. One young man, Derek, talked about how difficult it was the first day to take the first step and kneel down. He spoke about how he looked down the hallway and made eye contact with Troy and then how he watched as Troy knelt down to begin to pray.

What happens when 8th grade boys pray?
What would it take?

Realize that this is a busy hallway with students grabbing their books and having last minute conversations before class.

Realize as well that the kneeling was not designed to draw attention to themselves but designed to be somewhat inconspicuous and unassuming.

In fact, Derek said I was so nervous about doing it the first day that I purposely dropped my pen on the ground in front of my locker and then knelt down as if to pick it up and made it look like I was tying my shoe for a very long time. He laughed as he said, "I probably tied and untied my show about 3 or 4 times that first day."

As they told their story other students began to lean in and they asked the question, "so what happened?" "What prayers have you seen God answer so far?"

In the minds of the students gathered in the circle, there was not a sense that God may or desire to hear their prayers it was a matter of how soon would they begin to see changed lives?"

"Well," shot back one of the guys, "it has been getting easier and easier to continue to do it, but Mikey is the one who has the cool story." "Tell them what happened Mikey!"

Mikey was an interesting kid. He was a rather small 6th grader, but he was known for having a lot of exuberance and energy that was mostly powered by a massive amount of ADHD and yet up until this point he had sat quietly through the evening.

But prompted by these young men who were in the midst of sharing a common experience with him Mikey began his story.

One of the benefits (and potential issues) of ADHD in middle school boys is that because a lot of what occurs is based on impulse and without a lot of thinking Mikey did not need to put a lot of thought into participating in the 30-second drop.

For him, there was no need to fake tie his shoe or pretend to drop his pencil. He merely dropped to one knee and began to pray for the students who God had placed in his circle of influence on either side of his locker.

As Mikey began to explain how in his mind he was just like the other guys and had been participating all week one of the other older boys chimed in and cut him off by saying, "Yeah, but tell everyone who has the locker next to you."

In a somewhat understated way, Mikey named the name of that particular student (who for the purposes of the story we will call Bob), but Mike literally seemed to be oblivious as to why the older guys thought that it was a big deal or that he had anything unique to share.

Again, in a moment of shared ADD and to help out their younger friend who seemed to be missing the point of his own story another one of the 8th graders blurted out,

"You all need to understand. This kid is about twice to three times the size of Mike. He is literally huge, and he is the biggest bully in school." "Now tell everyone what happened on Wednesday, the student added.

"Well, on Wednesday, I got to my locker and knelt down to start praying but when I looked up "Bob" was standing there over the top of me.

"Tell them what he said to you," asked Derek excitedly, and then added, "Wait until you hear this."

"Get up," Bob said. "What are you doing down there?"

Now one of the 10th-grade students who had been leaning in and listening intently asked the obvious question, "Were you scared?"

"I was terrified," proclaimed Troy, "and I only had to watch the whole thing happen as I was standing down the hall."

What happens when 8th grade boys pray?
What would it take?

"You mean other people saw this?" another one of the High School students asked incredulously.

"Oh by this time there was a huge crowd gathered around to see if Bob was going to kill him," added Derek. "Tell them what you told him, Mike."

"I'm praying," said Mike.

You could almost hear the whole room inhale and hold their collective breath as one student asked the question that everyone was thinking "What did he say?"

"He kinda laughed and just asked, what I was praying for," said Mike.

"What did you say?" asked another high school student.

"I told him," I told him that I was praying for him and for everyone else in our school."

"And what did he say?" asked another one of the high school students?

"You won't believe this! Tell him what he said Mike!" Derek said barely being able to withhold his excitement.

"He looked at me and said, 'Well don't let me stop you. Get back down there and finish up. I could use some prayer right now."

As the entire room collectively leaned back and exhaled, I immediately felt prompted by the Holy Spirit to ask, "Is there anyone here who would like to pray for these guys and for Bob and Mikey as they move into this next week."

Immediately several of the 8th-grade guys raised their hands and said they wanted to pray and almost in the same breath Mike raised his hand and said he wanted to pray specifically for Bob and enough high school students all chimed in with their hands that it seemed like half or more of the room wanted to pray.

During that season, it had been considered normal during that season for us to break into small groups to afford everyone the opportunity to pray but I believe the Spirit prompted me to allow this instance to remain as a large group. So I looked at Derek and said, "why don't you start since it is your school, and then anyone else that feels led can chime in."

In the next several minutes' students began to passionately pour out their hearts to Jesus praising Him for what He was doing at this middle school and interceding on behalf of students and teachers. What I had not realized until that moment was that many of the high school students had attended that particular middle school and were familiar with the very same hallways and culture where these students were praying. In fact, even our high school students were familiar with Bob and his reputation.

But then something happened that was completely unplanned and unforeseen.
As we closed in prayer and began to look up one of the senior girls spoke up and asked, "Can I say something?"

"I am feeling so convicted right now listening to these guys tell their stories." She continued, "I am a senior. I am a student leader in my high school chapter of FCA (Fellowship of Christian Athletes), and I was all excited and feeling a little bit of pride because I was so daring that I asked my Pastor to come and speak to our students last week.
But now, after hearing them tell their story, I realize that have been caring more about my own reputation than about the peers at my school who do not know Jesus. I have been afraid to take a stand like that in my school."

Choking back tears, she said, "and I just want to confess this out loud to all of you right now and to ask you to pray that God will give me courage and that He will show me how He wants me to actually reflect Him genuinely this year and not just in my own little ways that will make me happy."

What happens when 8th grade boys pray?
What would it take?

Then moved, by the conviction of the Holy Spirit of God she could hold back her tears no longer and placing her head in her hands began to quietly sob.

Immediately, a few of the girls in her area of the room surrounded her and began to pray quietly over her. And I felt led to transition the time from large group to small group prayer and just said something to the effect of; "It seems like a good time to invite you to get into groups and to pray for each other about whatever the Lord has encouraged you to pray for.
Those of you who have been here in the past know how we do this. Others of you who are perhaps here for the first time, it's pretty simple if you want someone to pray for you just turn to the person next to you and ask."

The truth is that I really didn't need to say anything and I actually can't remember what I said. It was probably something like that, but I know that I didn't say much before the whole room was broken out into small groups of students calling out to God and interceding on behalf of each other and their friends.

As the evening continued I remember a female student coming to get me. "I need your help," she said, "There is a new girl, and she has just confessed to me that she has been having a lesbian relationship with another girl but feels convicted that it is wrong. We have been praying together, and she just told me that she wants to know how to become a Christian."

"Well," I said, "you know how to lead her to Christ, why do you need me?"

"I'm not sure, but I feel like I need help. Can you come?"

"Sure," I replied as I scanned the room and saw students in small groups of prayer filling the floor of the room, "but can you also find Mrs. Mason. I think it would be good if she were there too."

Mrs. Mason was an older soft-spoken and incredibly godly woman who had joined our student ministry leadership team nearly a year earlier.

To be honest, I had my doubts the first time that I met her. She did not exactly fit the conventional mold for a student ministry leader.

When we met, she spoke to me so softly that I literally needed to lean in to hear her words, "Chris," she said, "I just want you to know that I really have a heart for all students, but specifically for those who make bad choices and are angry at God.

"You know the type," she continued.

"The ones that are typically in the most trouble because they are acting out for some reason. I want to help in any way that I can but could you please do me a favor and if you find some students like that could you please feel free to send them in my direction?"

Stereotypically, she appeared more like the type of woman you expected to open the door and offer her grandchildren cookies and a nice cold glass of milk than the kind of woman who would have wanted to be surrounded by the type of students that she was describing, but I nodded my head yes and had no idea what a gem of a woman God had privileged me to just meet.

Finishing my scan of the room and coming to the conclusion that everything was okay for me to leave, I looked over to the door and began to follow my student to where this young lady was sitting out in the hallway. Nearing the doorway, in God's perfect timing, Mrs. Mason emerged through the door from the hall walking toward us.

"Great to see you!" I exclaimed with a sigh of relief, "are you available? I think we need you."

"I was just coming to see if you needed something, everything seems fine out in the hallways, where can I help?" she asked.

"Follow us, and I will explain on the way," I replied.

What happens when 8th grade boys pray?
What would it take?

Turning the corner the three of us, Mrs. Mason, the student and myself saw a 10th-grade student sitting quietly cross-legged on the floor with her hands folded in her lap. Then after brief introductions, we asked her to tell us her story.

In light of the context, I was thankful that both Mrs. Mason and the other female student were there and to be honest, I realized that there really was not much for me to do as Mrs. Mason began to lead this precious student through the steps of understanding the Gospel of Jesus.

But then as I began to internally debate whether or not it was good for me to stay or if I should quietly excuse myself another student approached and signaled me to come over.

This time it was the senior girl who had shared her conviction and requested prayer from her peers.

"Do you have a second?" she asked?

"What's up? What do you need?" I responded.

"Well, there is a student down in the youth room who is crying, and he just asked if I could find you so that he could talk with you. Do you have time?" she asked.

"Do you know why, or what is going on," I asked.

"No, but he is crying pretty hard, and he asked for you."

"Okay, thanks for letting me know," I said as I scanned the hallway and saw Mrs. Mason and the girls were now bowing their heads in prayer together and it appeared that she was leading the student through the process of receiving Christ's gift of forgiveness and salvation.

This is weird, I thought to myself. Nowhere in any of my youth ministry classes did we have a unit about how to handle an evening like this. And the weirdest part was that it was becoming the norm. My head was swimming as I recognized my dependence upon the Spirit of God and walked back into the youth room.

At that time we had a set of really nice restaurant booths with leather seats that lined the outer wall of our youth room, and I could see the student laying out on one of them face down with his head buried in his hands as he sobbed.

Praying silently as I walked, I grabbed a nearby box of tissues and set them on the table as I sat quietly in the booth on the other side of the table. For what had to be like 10-15 minutes or perhaps even longer I sat quietly as the young man cried out his heart on the bench across from me.

Finally, he reached his limit and slowly began to sit up. His eyes caught the tissue box, and he reached out with thankfulness to grab a few tissues and start to regain his composure. His eyes and face were blotchy and red from his prolonged tears.

I waited as he continued to sniffle and catch his breath and then finally asked the obvious question, "Are you okay? Is something wrong?"

Apparently, they must have taught me that question in the counseling class that I never took. In retrospect, it seems like a pretty idiotic question, but at the time it was the only one that I knew how to ask.

"No," he replied through continued sniffles and a few attempts to catch his breath, "I'm fine."

A bit incredulous at the paradox in his response, I pressed in a bit more, "Are you sure, is there anything going on that you want to talk with someone about?" "Mary said that you wanted to speak with me."

Wordlessly, he nodded his head slowly, but the movement was enough to almost make him start fully crying again.

Quietly, I waited while he again regained composure enough to speak, and then it seemed to take everything he had to say each word carefully enough to be understood but with enough pauses to ensure that he could complete the thought without getting lost again in his tears he stated the following.

What happens when 8th grade boys pray?
What would it take?

"Everything is fine. But I heard about this place, and I wanted to come here tonight because I have been reading the book of Acts at home by myself and it is confusing to me." He paused to gather himself and then continued, "It is confusing because I read the Bible and the book of Acts and I wonder to myself why my church does not feel like the church that I read about in the Bible."

"I've been asking my mom about it, and she said that God just doesn't work that way anymore. And yet I don't want to believe that so I've been asking God to show me that He is still alive and that the God of the Bible is still the God of today and then tonight I came here and met all of these students..." His voice trailed off, and he began choking back sobs again.

I waited and then after a little bit of time, I asked, "Did something happen tonight? Was someone mean to you? Did we do something wrong?" My mind raced as I searched for what I might have missed or who might have been the knucklehead that inadvertently said something to cause this young man so much pain.

"No," he replied. "That's not it at all!" "It's the exact opposite. When I came here tonight and witnessed what was going on it was just like I've been reading in the book of Acts. I think this is the way that church is supposed to be and I'm so happy!

With those words, he could not hold back anymore, and he burst into another round of sobs that lasted another 10-15 minutes while I sat back into my side of the booth in stunned silence as I watched the Holy Spirit of God minister to this young man's heart in front of me.

Is this the way the church is supposed to be?

I'd love to tell you that God continued to work in that church and soon the entire community was experiencing the unexplainable joy that young man expressed to me that evening. I'd love to tell you that what was happening on Friday nights in the youth room was carried over into Sunday mornings in the sanctuary but that would be more than an embellishment; it would be untrue.

The truth is that things were like the book of Acts in both the good and the bad ways.

Students would go on and continue their 30-second drops and other efforts to reflect Christ in their circles of influence in their schools and on their club sports teams.

Inspired by the 30-second drop, a group of male middle school students began a ministry they lovingly called "lunches with losers."

It's funny how God works, because there was not a concerted effort to start a ministry but one day while exiting the lunch line some of the students who were athletically inclined and held middle school social status as "cool kids" at the middle school where the 30-second drop was already taking place were looking for new ways to intentionally reflect Christ at their school.

Scanning the lunch room one of the young men saw a table where a number of students who had been labeled by their peers at school as "losers" and held the status of social outliers were sitting and led by the Spirit of God he walked over to their table and asked permission to join them for lunch.

Incredulously and waiting for the punch line the students asked why a person with his social status would be interested in sitting at the loser table with them.

Without missing a beat and in words that confirm the Words of Christ in the Gospels that the Spirit of God will give us the words to say, this young man looked the table squarely in the eye and replied, "I'm a Christian, which makes me a loser too, and if you allow me to sit with you maybe we can get to know each other, and I can tell you about who Jesus is and how He is changing my life."

What happens when 8th grade boys pray?
What would it take?

When he relayed the story to me, I could only sit back in my seat and mutter one word, "Wow!"

"So what has happened since then?" I asked.

"Well, word has gotten out around school, and now we have two tables filled up with people, and everyone is starting to call it lunch with the losers. But you wouldn't believe it, we call it lunch with the losers, but these are all really cool kids," he stated excitedly utterly unaware of the irony as he was surprised by his insightful discovery.

It would be correct to say that students were being saved and added to our number on a weekly basis. It would also be accurate to say that there were countless similar cool stories of students who intentionally chose to reflect Christ in circles of influence and as a result cultures were changing as students and teachers were both being impacted. But it would also be accurate to say that as in the book of Acts not everyone was happy about what was taking place. And like in the book of Acts there were a group of religious folk who could not understand why students would be doing crazy things like giving up social status to have lunch with the losers.

And like in the book of Acts persecution would eventually scatter the core of leaders as people with power and authority decided it was better for the students to move things back into a more conventional model that could be understood and controlled.

I was unprepared for the first part of the story because I had no context for what experiencing life and church in the books of Acts was actually all about. I was even less prepared for the pain of persecution as I watched the enemy of God scatter my team and take swipes at vulnerable young believers who were earnestly seeking God.

In retrospect, I wish I had had a better understanding of the book of Acts in order to have a slightly better grasp on what to expect.

Acts is a historical book that follows the Gospel accounts of the life of Christ.

Acts records the mission of God in action after the death, burial, and resurrection of Christ. Acts is the history of Christ and culture and the transformation that occurred as the two came in contact with each other through the witness and reflection of the early followers of Jesus.

While new cultures from around the world are being introduced to the life-changing message of Christ, those who were the message bearers were wrestling with their own cultural identity.

The early believers were not only experiencing a spiritual transition many were also in transition from a life as traditional Jewish disciples to Messianic Ambassadors for Christ. This was a radical cultural and life-changing shift that would cause ripples and shockwaves around the world. Some would embrace the cultural shift while others would fight against it until the enemies of the status quo would have their very lives stripped from them.

But for those who chose to allow Christ to impact the culture of their lives they would literally shed their cultural identity until the point of becoming self-described aliens and strangers in the culture that they have known.

All of this was just as radical at the time it took place as it seems to be now, but before we jump directly into the book of Acts and the story of how the disciples received the instructions of their co-mission with Christ it is essential for us to gain some context of that particular moment in the lives of the disciples.

To do that we need to go back 40 days before the ascension of Christ in heaven and 40 days before the invitation to co-mission with Christ in Acts 1:8 and revisit the group of disciples who were literally only days from experiencing one of their biggest failures in life.

What would it take for God to accomplish His mission in our culture?

Why is it so difficult?

My best class ever

Part I. Individual

1   What was the best class I have ever been a part of?

2   What made it the best class ever?

3   What did the teacher do to make it the best class ever?

4   What did I do to make it the best class ever?

5   What did the other students in the class do to make it the best class ever?

Part II. Pair and Share

1   Three ideas I heard from someone else that I really liked include:

2   One thing I think we should commit to as a class in order to make this the best class ever would be:

Breakfast on the Beach
John 21

The book of Acts begins with the reality of the resurrection.

Jesus has risen from the dead, and He is spending forty days with his disciples giving them last minute instructions before He ascends into heaven and they are released to join Him in bringing the glory of God to the ends of the earth.

This is a critical period of time in the life of this handful of world-changers who are going out into various cultures with the counter-cultural message of a resurrected Messiah.

But just before the beginning of the storyline of Acts and just before the reality of the resurrection this same group of disciples experienced one of the most significant individual and collective failures in their lives. A failure that no doubt left them struggling with doubt, shame, fear, and regret because in their moment of greatest testing they had each individually abandoned and denied their rabbi. The one that they had each personally pledged their lives to follow and imitate. The rabbi who they had walked with and talked with for literally every waking hour for the past two and a half years from the rising of the sun until late into the evenings.

What could have been their most significant moment of solidarity prior to the greatest moment in world history became something else? Something less.

The truth is that their individual and collective disgrace from their actions could have proven to be a fatal blow to their future participation in their relationship with their rabbi not to mention the mission He had recruited them to participate in. The memory of their failure could have replayed in their minds and plagued them to the point that they could have removed themselves as participants in the mission.

If you have been following Christ long enough, there is a strong possibility that you can relate to the disciples. Quite possibly there is a moment or moments where you know that you had the opportunity to take a stand and identify yourself with rabbi Jesus as your Messiah, but you remained quiet, took another option or even denied knowing Him altogether.

Still, others have experienced struggles of a different sort in our relationships with Jesus. Some of us have grown up in Christian homes or attended Christian schools for the majority of our lives and have wrestled with the idea of what it really means to be a Christian. Is it something that I have chosen or is it merely a result of my cultural upbringing?

Others have wrestled with the expectations of ourselves or others to live up to legalistic or religious standards and have found ourselves rebelling (if even quietly) against the stereotypes because we are not sure where the stereotype or expectations of others end and where the reality of a relationship with Jesus actually begins.

Still others of us have wrestled with doubt. Doubt about God; His existence, His truth, His revelation, His care, His concern and even whether or not we matter to Him at all.

The truth is that any of the possibilities on this list could have left us being able to identify even if in some small way with the close disciples of Jesus who felt like they should have known better but still wrestled with the confusion that accompanies disappointment, failure, and regret.

We were preparing in just a few short weeks or months to make the life-transition from high school into our next circle of influence for the kingdom of God. To us, It was less like we are moving into the culture as missionaries and ambassadors seeking to win ground for our Messiah and more like we are entering into a world that has already won a few battles in our lives.

We are inching ever so quickly into a life transition knowing full well that we have made mistakes and that we carry regrets. Some of us have fallen prey to public or private sin. Others have quietly struggled with personal additions. For some, our sins feel like they have been displayed before the world. For others, our prison holding us back from moving forward in our relationship with Christ and others in our memories and the battlefield is in our own mind.

Breakfast on the Beach
John 21

As a result, the invitation to move from a friend to a fisherman as co-participants in the mission to reflect the glory of God into our circles of influence feels less like the possibility of a vision and more like an impossible fantasy that we feel unqualified or even disqualified to participate in.

For some of us, the mission feels over before it has even gotten started. Like Peter and the other disciples who returned to the safe familiarity of their fishing boats and nets, our hearts are already making "fall back" plans for our own futures to ensure that we have a safety net. Following through on a vision for serving Christ feels too risky.

So whether it is the echo of the rooster crowing in your ear or the sounds of conventional wisdom that has you questioning your future role in the mission of God, there is a good chance that either your or a friend may be at a private crossroad that no one else is aware of.

It is in the context of this type of crossroad that we find Peter in John 21.

First, read and interact with the passage.

View the passage from the perspective of Peter. What would he have felt as he was back out on the water? It must have been humbling. Only a few days earlier he was walking into Jerusalem with His rabbi to celebrate the Passover meal, and now here he was back on the northern shores of the Galilee. As he looked out over the water it would have been possible for him to see the very mountainside where Jesus had taught the crowds, where he and the other disciples had participated in the feeding of the 5,000, where Jesus had calmed the storms and where less than a year ago he had actually walked out on the water himself.

He had shared in so many amazing moments that just a few years earlier he could never have dreamed about experiencing and yet here he was back on the water with his net in hand, and to make matters worse, he was unable to catch any fish.

Read John 21
Take notes and be prepared to share your insights and your questions with a small group.

1. What stands out to you as you read through the passage?

2. What can you relate to?

3. What seems foreign?

4. What questions does it raise?

Breakfast on the Beach
John 21

1 Later, Jesus appeared again to the disciples beside the Sea of Galilee. This is how it happened. 2 Several of the disciples were there—Simon Peter, Thomas (nicknamed the Twin), Nathanael from Cana in Galilee, the sons of Zebedee, and two other disciples.
3 Simon Peter said, "I'm going fishing."
"We'll come, too," they all said. So they went out in the boat, but they caught nothing all night.
4 At dawn Jesus was standing on the beach, but the disciples couldn't see who he was.
5 He called out, "Fellows, have you caught any fish?"
"No," they replied.
6 Then he said, "Throw out your net on the right-hand side of the boat, and you'll get some!" So they did, and they couldn't haul in the net because there were so many fish in it.
7 Then the disciple Jesus loved said to Peter, "It's the Lord!" When Simon Peter heard that it was the Lord, he put on his tunic (for he had stripped for work), jumped into the water, and headed to shore. 8 The others stayed with the boat and pulled the loaded net to the shore, for they were only about a hundred yards from shore. 9 When they got there, they found breakfast waiting for them—fish cooking over a charcoal fire, and some bread.
10 "Bring some of the fish you've just caught," Jesus said. 11 So Simon Peter went aboard and dragged the net to the shore. There were 153 large fish, and yet the net hadn't torn.
12 "Now come and have some breakfast!" Jesus said. None of the disciples dared to ask him, "Who are you?" They knew it was the Lord. 13 Then Jesus served them the bread and the fish. 14 This was the third time Jesus had appeared to his disciples since he had been raised from the dead.

15 After breakfast Jesus asked Simon Peter, "Simon son of John, do you love me more than these?"
"Yes, Lord," Peter replied, "you know I love you."
"Then feed my lambs," Jesus told him.
16 Jesus repeated the question: "Simon son of John, do you love me?"
"Yes, Lord," Peter said, "you know I love you."
"Then take care of my sheep," Jesus said.
17 A third time he asked him, "Simon son of John, do you love me?"
Peter was hurt that Jesus asked the question a third time. He said, "Lord, you know everything. You know that I love you."
Jesus said, "Then feed my sheep.
18 "I tell you the truth, when you were young, you were able to do as you liked; you dressed yourself and went wherever you wanted to go. But when you are old, you will stretch out your hands, and others will dress you and take you where you don't want to go." 19 Jesus said this to let him know by what kind of death he would glorify God. Then Jesus told him, "Follow me."
20 Peter turned around and saw behind them the disciple Jesus loved—the one who had leaned over to Jesus during supper and asked, "Lord, who will betray you?" 21 Peter asked Jesus, "What about him, Lord?"
22 Jesus replied, "If I want him to remain alive until I return, what is that to you? As for you, follow me." 23 So the rumor spread among the community of believers that this disciple wouldn't die. But that isn't what Jesus said at all. He only said, "If I want him to remain alive until I return, what is that to you?"
24 This disciple is the one who testifies to these events and has recorded them here. And we know that his account of these things is accurate.
25 Jesus also did many other things. If they were all written down, I suppose the whole world could not contain the books that would be written.

From Fisherman to Shepherd
John 21:9, 15-19

As you considered the passage in John 21 did you find it odd that in verse 9 Jesus not only had a fire, but he was also already cooking fish and bread.

Leave it to Jesus to have come prepared.

These guys had been fishing all night catching nothing at all and then with a word from their Master the nets were full of fish; and not just any fish but the type of fish that did not belong in the shallow waters of the northern Galilee.

Then as they landed on the shore dragging their heavy nets in the early morning light, they found that there was a fire already prepared for them on the beach. And on the coals were fish and some bread.

I don't know about you, but that is crazy to me.

And yet, as if that was not crazy enough - Jesus looks at them and invites them to bring their fish to the party before He asks them to sit down and eat.

Then Scripture records one of the most profound awkward silences of all times as the hungry disciples ate breakfast with their rabbi.

It is important to note that John identifies this as the third time that they had been in the presence of their risen Messiah. The number three and the breakfast of fish that had appeared from nowhere could not have been lost on the disciples as their minds raced and they continued to eat in silence.

My guess is that they were eating as much out of hunger as out of an attempt to fill the awkward space with activity.

My guess is that if Jesus could turn water into wine and have it be delicious and if he could multiply loaves and fishes in the past that the breakfast not only tasted fantastic but there was plenty to go around.

I chuckle to myself at the thought of Jesus tending the fire and while He watched the men eat and then seeing that one of them was getting close to the end of his fish or finishing off one of the pieces of bread Jesus reached out and asked the question, "Would you like some more?"

And all of this occurs before what is known as the reinstatement of Peter.

Throughout the next few verses in a scene that was reminiscent of Peter's denials of Christ, Jesus questions Peter's love three different times. The obvious take away is that Jesus is reinstating Peter and offering Peter the opportunity for forgiveness, reconciliation, and reinstatement but a more pressing underlying question is not whether or not Jesus forgives Peter but whether or not Peter will forgive himself.

Wracked with guilt, shame, embarrassment, and regret the once bold and brash disciple who had once walked on water had now returned to fishing in it.

Remember, Peter was already fully aware of the risen Christ. He had seen Him twice before. Peter was not back on the water because Jesus had failed to raise from the dead, he was back on the water because of the weight of his failure and regret.

The one who had claimed superior love and devotion and dreamed of fulfilling his rabbi's vision for his life of becoming a fisher of men had just come up empty handed after a night of fishing for tilapia. A night where he expected the sun to rise and for him to return home to sleep through the day in another attempt to forget the pain of the previous few weeks.

For Peter the forgiveness he received from Christ was just the beginning, the mercy he needed to move on with life was going to be the forgiveness he offered to himself.

Like Peter, there will come times in your life where you may feel paralyzed by your memories or harsh realities of personal failure in your relationship with Christ and His mission. Times when you may have chosen to stay silent when you were prompted to speak.

From Fisherman to Shepherd
John 21:9, 15-19

Perhaps a relationship has suffered or been broken because of betrayal or broken trust. Maybe you had the opportunity to stand tall, but you shrunk back. Maybe the pain of the past hits you in the face when you pass certain people in the hallway. Probably like Peter you have been guilty of betraying a friend and the person you find it difficult to forgive is yourself.

Now you find solace in the opportunity to count down the days until graduation or the next possible transition where you can leave the physical manifestations of the past behind.

Perhaps what you long to avoid are the expectations placed upon you from others that the change you long for in life is not possible and the friends and memories from the past are preventing you from embracing the person you want to become.

A few years ago, a student approached a colleague of mine during a time of reflection and sharing and said, "Nearly four years ago, I felt God stirring something in my heart. God was inviting me to deny myself and to serve Him with my high school years, and I shut Him down. Perhaps you have sensed the turmoil in my life. It was real. Because every time that God brought me back and reminded me of His invitation, I would rebelliously deny Him again and push Him away. Tonight, I want to apologize to you and God, and I want to commit to never rebel against His invitation again. I want to live on mission for God as I attend college and I do not want my next four years to look like my last four years."

It was a courageous statement for sure. But it was also tragic when you consider the amount of time that was lost. Certainly, it is noble to privately admit a wrong and invite a change at the end of four years, but would it not be legendary to for a student to take the same stand publicly and then ask their peers to help hold them accountable to the change with a full semester left?

Wouldn't there be something to be said if a student chose to give themselves the privilege of a full semester in order to leave going out on top with several months of gradual growth and victory and without any regrets rather than to slump out of school at with a last-minute confession and a pile of hope for a change in the future?

Perhaps before we can embrace the opportunity to take Christ to foreign cultures beyond the walls of our present situation we must embrace the Christ who can break us out of the culture that we have created for ourselves over the course the past 18 years; a culture that holds many of us captive to false beliefs, fears and attitudes from our past.

Perhaps for some of us, our first step is to accept an invitation to breakfast on the beach.

A breakfast where past failures become forgiven; a breakfast where youthful brashness is replaced with mature boldness; a breakfast where the fallen comes filled and where a fisherman becomes a shepherd.

This is the breakfast that Peter was invited to partake in prior to where the story of his life and ministry begins. It is a breakfast where Jesus does the fishing and supplies the meal, and it is a breakfast where the invitation moves from fishing for men to shepherding sheep.

It is perhaps one of the final movements in our circular journey to become reflections of Christ in every area of our life. It is the journey where the fisherman becomes forgiven, and the forgiven becomes the shepherd.

Before you journey any further into this semester or any closer to your next life transition take this opportunity to invite God to examine your heart. Where are the places that you need healing? Where are the areas where you need forgiveness? Where are the places where you need to stop running from an invitation and embrace the opportunity to move forward in freedom?

From Fisherman to Shepherd
John 21:9, 15-19

Peter's restorative breakfast with Jesus was in the context of a small group of friends. Friends who knew where he had been and who were willing to make the journey with him into the future.

Who are those people in your life that you can trust to make this next leg of your journey with as you prepare for the transition of life that is coming in just a few short months?

This final invitation and final movement as you accept the invitation to pick up the mission of God and to go into all the world and teach others is designed to be accomplished in the context of community.

In Acts 1, the disciples find themselves contemplating the kingdom with Christ for 40 days and then they spent the next 40 together with a small community and the word of God as their guide as they went through the final heart preparations for the transition into the next phase of their lives after Pentecost.

Bringing Christ to Culture is a team sport and in the same way that Acts is filled with teams of people who did life and ministered together out of their relationships with God and each other, you will need a team of people this semester to support you in your quest to finish well and prepare for your life transitions.

If you choose to invest your life, any part of it, into the work and ministry of the kingdom, then you must be prepared for the trials and tribulations that will inevitably ensue.

For Peter, Paul and the disciples in the book of Acts the attacks from those who thought of themselves as religious came immediately. The disciples were shunned, opposed, imprisoned and eventually martyred all in their efforts to introduce the life-changing mission of Christ into a resistant culture.

Be aware that if you choose to respond to the invitation of Christ to make a change in your life, there will be a ripple effect as you upset the status quo in the culture where you exist.

Like Peter, you can expect opposition from those who claim to be religious. Some may mock you. Others may turn their backs, and the enemy of God will be sure to hit you in the places where it will hurt the worst.

The reality of the decision in front of you and the potential consequences that await you on the other side may be enough for some to question whether or not it is better to bide their time and invite change in a new setting after this one and the risks associated has passed.

In light of that I want to encourage you with the words of the writer of the book of Hebrews who wrote, "Today, if you hear his voice, do not harden your hearts as you did in the rebellion" (Hebrews 3:15, 4:7).

In a similar manner, remember the words of Elijah to the people of Israel who were caught between a life of drought and famine connected to their lustful and sexual enslavement to idols of Baal and Asherah and a life connected to the mighty God who would send fire and rain from heaven when he asked, "How long will you waver between two opinions? For if the Lord is God, follow Him, but if Baal is God then follow Him (1 Kings 18:21).

Today as you take the Examine Assessment invite God to examine your heart and then if there is a moment of indecision ask yourself, "how long will you waiver?"

Do not wait, choose today who you will serve.

When you are done with the assessment answer the questions and fill out your plan for learning and then when you are finished read the assignment on the following page.

What would it take for God to accomplish His mission through us?

What steps will I take?

Examine™

SPIRITUAL FORMATION TOOL

ChristCenteredDiscipleship.com

"Everyone ought to examine themselves before
they eat of the bread and drink from the cup."

1 Corinthians 11:28, NLT

Wheaton Press
Train. Equip. Reflect.

Where are you?
Read. Respond. Reflect.

Directions: Read through the verses below and highlight or underline any words or phrases that seem to reflect or resonate with where you are at.

Skeptic. Presented with the person of Christ and the gospel multiple times, I demonstrate disinterest or unbelief.
"Even after Jesus had performed so many signs in their presence, they still would not believe in him." John 12:37, NIV
Characteristics: Calloused heart, dull ears, closed eyes.
"[F]or this people's heart has grown callous, their ears are dull of hearing, they have closed their eyes." Mt 13:15a, WEB
Christ's Next-Step Invitation: Repent. Believe.
"Then he began to denounce the cities in which most of his mighty works had been done, because they didn't repent." Matthew 11:20 ,WEB
Growth Barrier: A lack of spiritual understanding.
"When anyone hears the message about the kingdom and does not understand it, the evil one comes and snatches away what was sown in their heart. This is the seed sown along the path." Matthew 13:19, NIV
Spiritual Need: A loving and praying friend, a change of mind and heart initiated by the Holy Spirit.
"He said to them, 'This kind can come out by nothing, except by prayer and fasting.'" Mark 9:29, WEB
"As for you, you were dead in your transgressions and sins, in which you used to live when you followed the ways of this world and of the ruler of the kingdom of the air, the spirit who is now at work in those who are disobedient." Ephesians 2:1-2, NIV

Seeker. Questioning, with a desire to learn more about Jesus.
"He answered, 'And who is he, sir? Tell me, so that I may believe in him.'" John 9:36, ISV
Characteristics: A ready heart, open ears, questions with an interest to learn more about Jesus.
"Again, the next day, John was standing with two of his disciples, and he looked at Jesus as he walked, and said, 'Behold, the Lamb of God!' The two disciples heard him speak, and they followed Jesus. Jesus turned, and saw them following, and said to them, 'What are you looking for?' They said to him, 'Rabbi' (which is to say, being interpreted, Teacher), 'where are you staying?' He said to them, 'Come, and see.' They came and saw where he was staying, and they stayed with him that day. It was about the tenth hour." John 1:35-39, WEB
Christ's Next-Step Invitation: Repent. Believe.
"Now after John was taken into custody, Jesus came into Galilee, preaching the Good News of God's Kingdom, and saying, 'The time is fulfilled, and God's Kingdom is at hand! Repent, and believe in the Good News.'" Mark 1:14-15, WEB
Growth Barrier: A lack of clear presentation and understanding of the Gospel, a lack of invitation.
"How, then, can people call on someone they have not believed? And how can they believe in someone they have not heard about? And how can they hear without someone preaching?" Romans 10:14, ISV
Spiritual Need: A clear gospel presentation and an invitation to believe and receive salvation.
"But to all who did receive him, who believed in his name, he gave the right to become children of God." John 1:12, ESV

Believer. Presented with the Gospel I believe.
He said, "Lord, I believe!" and he worshiped him. John 9:38 WEB
Characteristics: Seed begins to germinate, shallow soil, little or no roots.
Other seeds fell on rocky ground, where they did not have much soil, and immediately they sprang up, since they had no depth of soil, but when the sun rose they were scorched. And since they had no root, they withered away. Matthew 13:5-6
Christ's Next Step Invitation: Follow.
And he said to them, "Follow me, and I will make you fishers of men." Matthew 4:19 ESV
Growth Barrier: Lack of roots, lack of knowledge, testing, trouble, persecution.
These in the same way are those who are sown on the rocky places, who, when they have heard the word, immediately receive it with joy. They have no root in themselves, but are short-lived. When oppression or persecution arises because of the word, immediately they stumble. Mark 4:16-17 WEB
Spiritual Need: Prayer, roots, knowledge, biblical teaching, time, worship and someone to walk with them.
Like newborn infants, long for the pure spiritual milk, that by it you may grow up into salvation. 1 Peter 2:2 ESV
So then, just as you received Christ Jesus as Lord, continue to live your lives in him, rooted and built up in him, strengthened in the faith as you were taught, and overflowing with thankfulness. Colossians 2:6-7 NIV
We continually ask God to fill you with the knowledge of His will through all the wisdom and understanding that the Spirit gives, so that you may live a life worthy of the Lord and please Him in every way: bearing fruit in every good work, growing in the knowledge of God, being strengthened with all power according to His glorious might so that you may have great endurance and patience, and giving joyful thanks to the Father, who has qualified you to share in the inheritance of His holy people in the kingdom of light. Colossians 1:9-12 NIV

Follower. Growing in faith and love; deepening roots and knowledge; struggling with thorns, trials, forgiveness, doubt, and perseverance.

"By this all people will know that you are my disciples, if you have love for one another." John 13:35, ESV

Characteristics: Beginning to push through the soil, struggling with thorns and weeds.

"Others fell among thorns. The thorns grew up and choked them." Matthew 13:7, WEB

"And calling the crowd to him with his disciples, he said to them, 'If anyone would come after me, let him deny himself and take up his cross and follow me.'" Mark 8:34, ESV

Christ's Next-Step Invitation: Deny self; pick up cross; trust, obey, and love Christ and others.

"Then Jesus said to his disciples, "If anyone desires to come after me, let him deny himself, and take up his cross, and follow me." Matthew 16:24, WEB

Growth Barrier: Thorns, worries of this life, doubt, deceitfulness of wealth, comfort, self and self-will.

"Others are those who are sown among the thorns. These are those who have heard the word, and the cares of this age, and the deceitfulness of riches, and the lusts of other things entering in choke the word, and it becomes unfruitful." Mark 4:18-19,

Spiritual Need: Deny self; trials; endurance, perseverance, time, small group relationships, and accountability.

"Consider it pure joy, my brothers and sisters, whenever you face trials of many kinds, because you know that the testing of your faith produces perseverance. Let perseverance finish its work so that you may be mature and complete, not lacking anything." James 1:2-4, NIV

"Through him we have also obtained access by faith into this grace in which we stand, and we rejoice in hope of the glory of God. Not only that, but we rejoice in our sufferings, knowing that suffering produces endurance, and endurance produces character, and character produces hope." Romans 5:2-4, ESV

"These have come so that the proven genuineness of your faith—of greater worth than gold, which perishes even though refined by fire—may result in praise, glory and honor when Jesus Christ is revealed." 1 Peter 1:7, NIV

Friend. Marked by obedient love for Christ and others; may wrestle with isolation, complacency and accountability.

"You are my friends if you do what I command you." John 15:14, ESV

Characteristics: Good soil, obedience to Christ, fruit, growing faith, increasing love and perseverance in trials.

"We ought always to thank God for you, brothers and sisters, and rightly so, because your faith is growing more and more, and the love all of you have for one another is increasing. Therefore, among God's churches we boast about your perseverance and faith in all the persecutions and trials you are enduring." 2 Thessalonians 1:3-4, NIV

Christ's Next-Step Invitation: Love, obey, go, teach.

"If you love me, you will keep my commandments." John 14:15, ESV

"Jesus came to them and spoke to them, saying, 'All authority has been given to me in heaven and on earth. Go, and make disciples of all nations, baptizing them in the name of the Father and of the Son and of the Holy Spirit, teaching them to observe all things that I commanded you. Behold, I am with you always, even to the end of the age.' Amen." Mt 28:18-20,

Growth Barrier: Complacency, fear, pride, lack of vision and lack of equipping.

"Then he said to his disciples, 'The harvest indeed is plentiful, but the laborers are few.'" Matthew 9:37, WEB

"How, then, can people call on someone they have not believed? And how can they believe in someone they have not heard about? And how can they hear without someone preaching?" Romans 10:14, ISV

Spiritual Need: Vision, continued obedience, equipping, empowerment, continued spurring and accountability within community.

" ... to equip his people for works of service, so that the body of Christ may be built up until we all reach unity in the faith and in the knowledge of the Son of God and become mature, attaining to the whole measure of the fullness of Christ." Ephesians 4:12-13, NIV

"As for you, brothers, do not grow weary in doing good." 2 Thessalonians 3:13, ESV

"Let us continue to hold firmly to the hope that we confess without wavering, for the one who made the promise is faithful. And let us continue to consider how to motivate one another to love and good deeds, not neglecting to meet together, as is the habit of some, but encouraging one another even more as you see the day of the Lord coming nearer." Hebrews 10:23-25, ISV

Fisherman. Reflecting Christ and reproducing fruit of righteousness and good works.

"Because we have heard of your faith in Christ Jesus and of the love you have for all God's people—the faith and love that spring from the hope stored up for you in heaven and about which you have already heard in the true message of the gospel that has come to you. In the same way, the gospel is bearing fruit and growing throughout the whole world—just as it has been doing among you since the day you heard it and truly understood God's grace." Colossians 1:4-6, NIV

Characteristics: Good soil, fruitfulness, harvest, influence, reflecting Christ.

"Others fell on good soil, and yielded fruit: some one hundred times as much, some sixty, and some thirty." Mt 13:8, WEB

Christ's Next-Step Invitation: Teach others.

"Therefore, as you go, disciple people in all nations, baptizing them in the name of the Father, and the Son, and the Holy Spirit, teaching them to obey everything that I've commanded you." Matthew 28:19-20a, ISV

Growth Barrier: Complacency, fear, pride, lack of vision, lack of equipping, weariness.

"Let's not get tired of doing what is good, for at the right time we will reap a harvest—if we do not give up." Galatians 6:9, ISV

"Think about the one who endured such hostility from sinners, so that you may not become tired and give up." Heb 12:3,

Spiritual Need: Perseverance, humility, faithfulness, accountability, reliable people.

"It gave me great joy when some believers came and testified about your faithfulness to the truth, telling how you continue to walk in it." 3 John 3, NIV

"And what you have heard from me in the presence of many witnesses entrust to faithful men who will be able to teach others also." 2 Timothy 2:2, ESV

Examine™ Spiritual Formation Planning Tool

More resources available at WheatonPress.com

Directions: Answer the following seven questions using the words or phrases you highlighted or underlined.

1. Where am I?
   Skeptic. When presented with the gospel, I do not believe.
   Seeker. Questioning, with a desire to learn more about Jesus.
   Believer. Presented with the gospel, I chose to believe.
   Follower. Growing in faith, love, and roots. Struggling with thorns, trials, and perseverance.
   Friend. Marked by obedient love for Christ and others.
   Fisherman. Reflecting Christ and bearing fruit of righteousness and good works.

2. Where would I like to be in six months?
   Skeptic. When presented with the gospel, I do not believe.
   Seeker. Questioning, with a desire to learn more about Jesus.
   Believer. Presented with the Gospel, I chose to believe.
   Follower. Growing in faith, love, and roots. Struggling with thorns, trials, and perseverance.
   Friend. Marked by obedient love for Christ and others.
   Fisherman. Reflecting Christ and bearing fruit of righteousness and good works.

3. What invitation do I need to respond to in order to take my next step?
   Skeptic. Repent.
   Seeker. Repent. Believe.
   Believer. Follow.
   Follower. Deny self. Pick up cross. Obey. Love Christ and others.
   Friend. Love. Obey. Go.
   Fisherman. Teach others.

4. What barriers will I face?
   Skeptic. Calloused heart, deaf ears, closed eyes.
   Seeker. Lack of clear testimony. Lack of invitation.
   Believer. Lack of root. Testing. Trouble. Persecution.
   Follower. Thorns. Worries of this life. Deceitfulness of wealth. Comfort. Self.
   Friend. Complacency. Fear. Lack of vision. Lack of equipping.
   Fisherman. Complacency. Fear. Lack of vision. Lack of equipping. Weariness.

5. What spiritual needs do I have?
   Skeptic. Prayer. Repentance. A believing friend.
   Seeker. Receive. Believe. Salvation.
   Believer. Prayer. Roots. Knowledge. Teaching. Worship. Time.
   Follower. Deny self. Trials. Endurance. Perseverance. Time. Small group relationships and accountability.
   Friend. Vision. Continued obedience. Equipping. Opportunity. Empowerment. Accountability within community.
   Fisherman. Perseverance. Faithfulness. Reliable people.

6. What steps will I take?

7. Who will I ask to hold me accountable?

What would it take for God to accomplish His mission in me?
What steps will I take?

Assignment

Three Letters

After completing your Examine Assessment, your assignment is to write three letters.

      1. The first letter is to your future self one year after graduation.

      2. The second letter is to your future self five years after graduation.

      3. The third letter is to your future self ten years after graduation.

In each letter outline to yourself a reminder of who you are now and the commitments that you are making to God and yourself about finishing off this next season of your life well. Then inform yourself about whom you are asking Him to make you into at that season in your life. Do not focus on what you want to do with your life as much as focusing on who you believe God is inviting you to become. Who is it that God is inviting you to become as you accept the invitations to move through the stages toward spiritual maturity?

- If you get married then what type of spouse do you desire to become?
- How will you reflect Christ to your future spouse?
- If you become a parent then how do you desire to reflect Christ to your future children?
- What do you want your life to be marked by?

As now - so then

Many years ago when I was in my last semester of high school, a mentor taught me the "as now so then" principle of life. The basis for the principle is that the decisions you make today will influence the person you will be tomorrow. In simple terms, if you work out today, then you will be fit tomorrow. Similarly, if you eat a lot of fat, greasy food today, then the odds are that you will become a fat, greasy dude in the days to come.

The same principle of as now – so then applies to our spiritual lives as we seek to be transformed into the people we will become tomorrow. If we put off making the first hard decision today thinking that it will become easier tomorrow, then we are merely fooling ourselves. Your final step in this project is to reverse engineer the process and plan for who you will become according to the as now – so then principle.

- What steps do you need to commit to begin taking today?
- What invitations of Christ do you need to begin taking today?
- Who will you tell and invite to hold you accountable for your first set of steps during this semester?

Be specific as you consider and write out your response and then put together a personal action plan that takes into consideration who you are asking God to lead you to become in the future.

Self Interview

Name:

1   What was the cultural giant that you believe our generation is facing?

2   What do you think would or could be a Christ-centered solution to that giant?

3   What is (or do you think) some of the cultural pressure that would be faced in the process of implementing that solution?

4   Is there anyone that you know who is attempting to implement the solution Describe their journey?

5   Describe the eternal mission of God for the earth?

6   What are some of the events or circumstances that God has used in your life to prepare you to participate in His eternal mission?

7   Describe your vision for the rest of your life?

33

Parent Interview

Name:

1   What was the cultural giant that you believe our generation is facing?

2   What do you think would or could be a Christ-centered solution to that giant?

3   What is (or do you think) some of the cultural pressure that would be faced in the process of implementing that solution?

4   Is there anyone that you know who is attempting to implement the solution Describe their journey?

5   Describe the eternal mission of God for the earth?

6   What are some of the events or circumstances that God has used in your life to prepare you to participate in His eternal mission?

7   Describe your vision for the rest of your life?

Peer Interview

Name:

1   What was the cultural giant that you believe our generation is facing?

2   What do you think would or could be a Christ-centered solution to that giant?

3   What is (or do you think) some of the cultural pressure that would be faced in the process of implementing that solution?

4   Is there anyone that you know who is attempting to implement the solution Describe their journey?

5   Describe the eternal mission of God for the earth?

6   What are some of the events or circumstances that God has used in your life to prepare you to participate in His eternal mission?

7   Describe your vision for the rest of your life?

Peer Interview

Name:

1   What was the cultural giant that you believe our generation is facing?

2   What do you think would or could be a Christ-centered solution to that giant?

3   What is (or do you think) some of the cultural pressure that would be faced in the process of implementing that solution?

4   Is there anyone that you know who is attempting to implement the solution describe their journey?

5   Describe the eternal mission of God for the earth?

6   What are some of the events or circumstances that God has used in your life to prepare you to participate in His eternal mission?

7   Describe your vision for the rest of your life?

How do I make sense of culture?

Integrated =   Integrity =   Disintegrated =

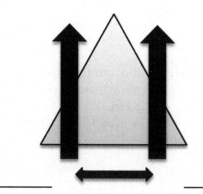
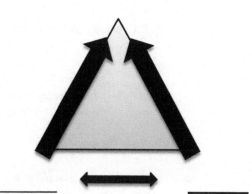

_____   _____   _____   _____

_____   _____

Why is culture disintegrated?
Small Group Project

Passage study: Genesis 1-3

a. Observations

b. What does it mean?

c. What are the implications?

Part II. Class Notes and Discussion

Everything is ultimately theological

In order to gain an accurate understanding of the impact of disintegration from a Theological perspective, perhaps it would be wise to examine the theological foundations.

1. What is it that is disintegrated?

2. And how did it get that way?

> So God created mankind in his own image, in the image of God he created them; male and female he created them…and God saw everything He had made, and it was very good.
> - Genesis 1:27, 31(NIV)

God Created the Material to reflect the _____.

He Created the Natural, to reflect the _____.

> So that there was nothing false and man, perfectly reflecting the image of God, was able to live in authentic, genuine reality – so that we experienced life…integrated.

Disintegration defined

a. How did disintegration occur?

b. How bad is it?

c. What is the solution?

What are the four foundational realities of integration?

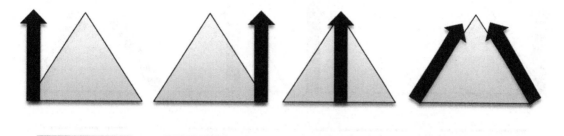

_____   _____   _____   _____

What is the impact of disintegration?
Small Group Project

Concept study: Romans 3:23, 1 Corinthians 4:4

a. Observations

b. What does it mean?

c. What are the implications?

Class Notes and Discussion

How does the impact of disintegration impact culture?

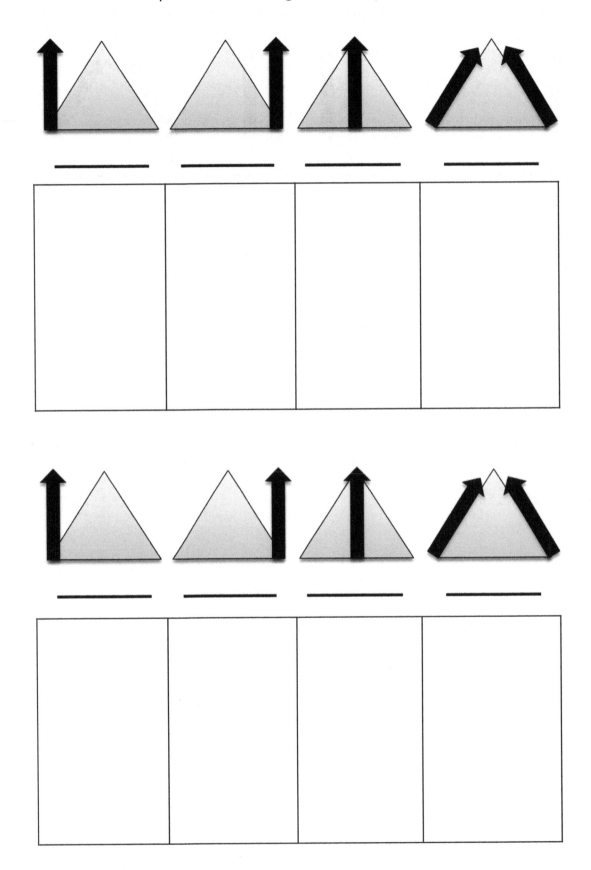

How do we reintegrate culture to reflect its intended purpose?
Small Group Project

Verse study: 2 Corinthians 3:18

And we all, who with unveiled faces contemplate the Lord's glory, are being transformed into his image with ever-increasing glory, which comes from the Lord, who is the Spirit.

a. Observations

b. What does it mean?

c. What are the implications?

Class Notes and Discussion

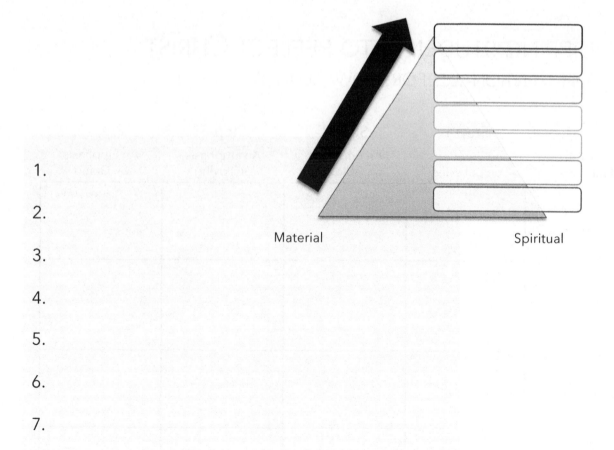

Material   Spiritual

1.

2.

3.

4.

5.

6.

7.

Will God accomplish His mission?
Small Group Project

Passage study: Revelation 8-9, 21-22

a. Observations

b. What does it mean?

c. What are the implications?

Class Notes and Discussion

EQUIPPING STUDENTS TO REFLECT CHRIST
AN INTENTIONAL EFFORT TOWARD INTEGRATION

Growth Emphasis	Step 1 An Emphasis on Believing	Step 2 An Emphasis on Following	Step 3 An Emphasis on Loving	Step 4 An Emphasis on Going
Essential Questions				
Essential Outcomes				
Courses:				
Leadership Pipeline				

Invited to co-mission
with the Messiah

Christ & Culture

The Promise of the Holy Spirit
Acts 1:1-5

Setting the context

1. Who is Theophilus?

2. Who is the writer of the letter?

3. What is the basis for the authority of the writer for writing this letter?

4. What was the first book that was written by the author and where did they get their source material?

In my first book I told you, Theophilus, about everything Jesus began to do and teach 2 until the day he was taken up to heaven after giving his chosen apostles further instructions through the Holy Spirit. 3 During the forty days after he suffered and died, he appeared to the apostles from time to time, and he proved to them in many ways that he was actually alive. And he talked to them about the Kingdom of God.

4 Once when he was eating with them, he commanded them, "Do not leave Jerusalem until the Father sends you the gift he promised, as I told you before. 5 John baptized with water, but in just a few days you will be baptized with the Holy Spirit."

5. What is the purpose of these two (or more) letters?

Reflect.

A. The disciples were instructed to wait in Jerusalem for 40 days. Describe a time when you have been instructed by God to wait for something. Describe the circumstances and the feelings that accompanied the period of time.

B. How did you time of waiting impact your relationship with God? What choices did you make during that time that were healthy? What choices did you make during that time that you would not repeat? Why?

C. Sometimes God allows for us to wait for Him by ourselves (Elijah in the wilderness) other times He allows for us to have the comfort of a community to help encourage and strengthen us (David in the wilderness). Why do you think God allowed the disciples to experience these 40 days in the context of a community? What difference do you think that made.

The Ascension of Jesus
Acts 1:6-11

6 So when the apostles were with Jesus, they kept asking him, "Lord, has the time come for you to free Israel and restore our kingdom?"
7 He replied, "The Father alone has the authority to set those dates and times, and they are not for you to know. 8 But you will receive power when the Holy Spirit comes upon you. And you will be my witnesses, telling people about me everywhere–in Jerusalem, throughout Judea, in Samaria, and to the ends of the earth."

9 After saying this, he was taken up into a cloud while they were watching, and they could no longer see him. 10 As they strained to see him rising into heaven, two white-robed men suddenly stood among them. 11 "Men of Galilee," they said, "why are you standing here staring into heaven? Jesus has been taken from you into heaven, but someday he will return from heaven in the same way you saw him go!"

Reflect.

1. Jesus invested 40 days retraining His disciples after the resurrection. One of the key items that He had to reteach them was the concept of the Kingdom of Heaven. Remember that even for the disciples that He was not the messiah that they "wanted" but the one that they needed. In other words, even after the resurrection they were still confused. They still thought that Jesus was going to set up an earthly kingdom that would deliver them from the Romans. What is the significance of how Christ responds to them regarding the future? How should His promise still impact our lives today?

2. Jesus makes a promise about the empowering of the Holy Spirit. What does it mean to live a life empowered by the Spirit of God? How do we know if we are living life under our own power or under the power of the Spirit? What is the difference?

3. Jesus uses His last words to reiterate the same mission that God gave to Adam, Noah, Abraham and that Solomon reiterated at the inauguration of the temple. What is the current state of that mission today? Where is the overall perspective of our generation with regards to ensuring the mission? What steps could we take to obey and apply the co-mission of Christ to our own lives or our own context?

4. What difference would it have made if the disciples would have disobeyed and refused to wait for the empowering of the Holy Spirit?

5. What would be the impact if we choose not to obey what the Spirit of God leads us to do?

Matthias Replaces Judas
Acts 1:12-26

12 Then the apostles returned to Jerusalem from the Mount of Olives, a distance of half a mile. 13 When they arrived, they went to the upstairs room of the house where they were staying.
Here are the names of those who were present: Peter, John, James, Andrew, Philip, Thomas, Bartholomew, Matthew, James (son of Alphaeus), Simon (the zealot), and Judas (son of James). 14 They all met together and were constantly united in prayer, along with Mary the mother of Jesus, several other women, and the brothers of Jesus.
15 During this time, when about 120 believers were together in one place, Peter stood up and addressed them. 16 "Brothers," he said, "the Scriptures had to be fulfilled concerning Judas, who guided those who arrested Jesus. This was predicted long ago by the Holy Spirit, speaking through King David. 17 Judas was one of us and shared in the ministry with us."
18 (Judas had bought a field with the money he received for his treachery. Falling headfirst there, his body split open, spilling out all his intestines.

19 The news of his death spread to all the people of Jerusalem, and they gave the place the Aramaic name Akeldama, which means "Field of Blood.")
20 Peter continued, "This was written in the book of Psalms, where it says, 'Let his home become desolate, with no one living in it.' It also says, 'Let someone else take his position.'
21 "So now we must choose a replacement for Judas from among the men who were with us the entire time we were traveling with the Lord Jesus— 22 from the time he was baptized by John until the day he was taken from us. Whoever is chosen will join us as a witness of Jesus' resurrection."
23 So they nominated two men: Joseph called Barsabbas (also known as Justus) and Matthias. 24 Then they all prayed, "O Lord, you know every heart. Show us which of these men you have chosen 25 as an apostle to replace Judas in this ministry, for he has deserted us and gone where he belongs." 26 Then they cast lots, and Matthias was selected to become an apostle with the other eleven.

Reflect.

The disciples are coming off of a major setback in their lives. Their rabbi has been crucified and they have denied knowing him or fled in fear.

Then the miraculous happens and Jesus is not only resurrected from the dead but He seeks them out a second time and offers them forgiveness and a new opportunity to follow Him.

For forty days He rebuilds them. Demonstrating His love and bringing understanding to His mission, His Kingdom and His grace.

Then He leaves them. But not without instruction. They are to wait as a community until a promise is fulfilled. Those days are not wasted.

What is the application for your life?

1. Have you ever experienced failure in your relationship with Christ?

2. Have you ever experienced "reinstatement" or a new invitation to follow and represent Him?

3. Who is your small group or community that you are choosing to "do life" life with as you encourage one another to follow Christ?

4. As you think about your next steps in life how is considering your part in the mission of God playing a part in your choices or decisions?

The Holy Spirit Comes
Acts 2:1-13

On the day of Pentecost all the believers were meeting together in one place. 2 Suddenly, there was a sound from heaven like the roaring of a mighty windstorm, and it filled the house where they were sitting. 3 Then, what looked like flames or tongues of fire appeared and settled on each of them. 4 And everyone present was filled with the Holy Spirit and began speaking in other languages, as the Holy Spirit gave them this ability.

5 At that time there were devout Jews from every nation living in Jerusalem. 6 When they heard the loud noise, everyone came running, and they were bewildered to hear their own languages being spoken by the believers.

7 They were completely amazed. "How can this be?" they exclaimed. "These people are all from Galilee, 8 and yet we hear them speaking in our own native languages! 9 Here we are— Parthians, Medes, Elamites, people from Mesopotamia, Judea, Cappadocia, Pontus, the province of Asia, 10 Phrygia, Pamphylia, Egypt, and the areas of Libya around Cyrene, visitors from Rome 11 (both Jews and converts to Judaism), Cretans, and Arabs. And we all hear these people speaking in our own languages about the wonderful things God has done!" 12 They stood there amazed and perplexed. "What can this mean?" they asked each other.

13 But others in the crowd ridiculed them, saying, "They're just drunk, that's all!"

Setting the context

1. What is the purpose of the Feast of Pentecost?

2. What is the significance of these events taking place of the feast of Pentecost?

3. Find passages in the Old Testament where God uses fire from heaven to represent His presence and filling. List them below.

4. In light of these Old Testament passage what is the significance of the "tongues of fire" that appeared over each of the believers who were assembled? What is the message that God was sending? How is that a dramatic shift from the way that God operated in the Old Testament?

5. What is the significance of the Holy Spirit empowering the believers to speak in other languages? (Hint: For help answering this question check out Genesis 10 and 11 and 12).

Peter Preaches to the Crowd
Acts 2:14-41

14 Then Peter stepped forward with the eleven other apostles and shouted to the crowd, "Listen carefully, all of you, fellow Jews and residents of Jerusalem! Make no mistake about this. 15 These people are not drunk, as some of you are assuming. Nine o'clock in the morning is much too early for that. 16 No, what you see was predicted long ago by the prophet Joel:

17 'In the last days,' God says,
  'I will pour out my Spirit upon all people.
Your sons and daughters will prophesy.
  Your young men will see visions,
  and your old men will dream dreams.

18 In those days I will pour out my Spirit
  even on my servants–men and women
  alike and they will prophesy.
19 And I will cause wonders in the heavens above and signs on the earth below–
  blood and fire and clouds of smoke.
20 The sun will become dark,
  and the moon will turn blood red
    before that great and glorious day of the Lord arrives.
21 But everyone who calls on the name of the Lord will be saved.'

22 "People of Israel, listen! God publicly endorsed Jesus the Nazarene by doing powerful miracles, wonders, and signs through him, as you well know. 23 But God knew what would happen, and his prearranged plan was carried out when Jesus was betrayed. With the help of lawless Gentiles, you nailed him to a cross and killed him. 24 But God released him from the horrors of death and raised him back to life, for death could not keep him in its grip.
25 King David said this about him:
'I see that the Lord is always with me.
  I will not be shaken, for he is right beside me.
26 No wonder my heart is glad,
  and my tongue shouts his praises!
  My body rests in hope.

27 For you will not leave my soul among the dead or allow your Holy One to rot in the grave.
28 You have shown me the way of life,
  and you will fill me with the joy of your presence.'
29 "Dear brothers, think about this! You can be sure that the patriarch David wasn't referring to himself, for he died and was buried, and his tomb is still here among us. 30 But he was a prophet, and he knew God had promised with an oath that one of David's own descendants would sit on his throne. 31 David was looking into the future and speaking of the Messiah's resurrection. He was saying that God would not leave him among the dead or allow his body to rot in the grave.
32 "God raised Jesus from the dead, and we are all witnesses of this. 33 Now he is exalted to the place of highest honor in heaven, at God's right hand. And the Father, as he had promised, gave him the Holy Spirit to pour out upon us, just as you see and hear today. 34 For David himself never ascended into heaven, yet he said,
'The Lord said to my Lord,
  "Sit in the place of honor at my right hand
35 until I humble your enemies,
  making them a footstool under your feet."'
36 "So let everyone in Israel know for certain that God has made this Jesus, whom you crucified, to be both Lord and Messiah!"
37 Peter's words pierced their hearts, and they said to him and to the other apostles, "Brothers, what should we do?"
38 Peter replied, "Each of you must repent of your sins and turn to God, and be baptized in the name of Jesus Christ for the forgiveness of your sins. Then you will receive the gift of the Holy Spirit. 39 This promise is to you, to your children, and to those far away–all who have been called by the Lord our God." 40 Then Peter continued preaching for a long time, strongly urging all his listeners, "Save yourselves from this crooked generation!"
41 Those who believed what Peter said were baptized and added to the church that day– about 3,000 in all.

Peter Preaches to the Crowd
Acts 2:14-41

Reflect.

1. Read through the sermon. Highlight or underline key elements.

2. What stand out to you about the sermon?

3. What stands out to you about the fact that it is Peter who is preaching the sermon? Why is that fact significant?

4. Remember that less 3 months earlier Peter had denied Christ in front of a handful of people in the middle of the night. Now it is the middle of the day and he is proclaiming that people should repent of their false ideas of who Jesus Christ is and was. In light of how God transformed Peter what is the application for your life. What is God inviting you to change your mind about? Regarding Him? Regarding yourself?

5. Read Exodus 32:27-29. What is the correlation between this passage and Acts 2:41? What is the message that God is sending by the 3,000 people who are saved on Pentecost?

The Believers Form a Community
Acts 2:42-47

Reflect.

After the events of Pentecost a new community is formed. In many ways this new community is the one that is designed to provide support and encouragement as the disciples move from friends of Christ to devoted fishermen who co-mission with Christ.

1. According to these verses what are the key markers of this new community? Highlight or underline each word of significance and then use those words and the space below to describe what life in this new community would have been like.

42 All the believers devoted themselves to the apostles' teaching, and to fellowship, and to sharing in meals (including the Lord's Supper), and to prayer.
43 A deep sense of awe came over them all, and the apostles performed many miraculous signs and wonders. 44 And all the believers met together in one place and shared everything they had. 45 They sold their property and possessions and shared the money with those in need. 46 They worshiped together at the Temple each day, met in homes for the Lord's Supper, and shared their meals with great joy and generosity— 47 all the while praising God and enjoying the goodwill of all the people. And each day the Lord added to their fellowship those who were being saved.

2. How is your description similar or different to what you experience or have experienced in your current relationships with other believers?

3. What would you like to change?

4. What steps would you be willing to take to make those changes?

Peter Heals A Crippled Beggar
Acts 3:1-11

Peter and John went to the Temple one afternoon to take part in the three o'clock prayer service. 2 As they approached the Temple, a man lame from birth was being carried in. Each day he was put beside the Temple gate, the one called the Beautiful Gate, so he could beg from the people going into the Temple. 3 When he saw Peter and John about to enter, he asked them for some money.

4 Peter and John looked at him intently, and Peter said, "Look at us!" 5 The lame man looked at them eagerly, expecting some money. 6 But Peter said, "I don't have any silver or gold for you. But I'll give you what I have. In the name of Jesus Christ the Nazarene, get up and walk!"

7 Then Peter took the lame man by the right hand and helped him up. And as he did, the man's feet and ankles were instantly healed and strengthened. 8 He jumped up, stood on his feet, and began to walk! Then, walking, leaping, and praising God, he went into the Temple with them.

9 All the people saw him walking and heard him praising God. 10 When they realized he was the lame beggar they had seen so often at the Beautiful Gate, they were absolutely astounded! 11 They all rushed out in amazement to Solomon's Colonnade, where the man was holding tightly to Peter and John.

Reflect.

As you read this passage it is helpful to remember that the disciples are still in Jerusalem and that the temple is where the Jews (not the Christians) meet to worship.

1. What is significant about the fact that Peter and John are going to worship in the Temple for the 3pm prayer service?

2. What is the purpose of this particular story of the lame man being healed? What is the connection to the person and the mission of Christ? (Helpful passages include: Isaiah 61, Luke 4:14-21).

3. Read and outline Isaiah 61:1-11, what prophecies are being fulfilled? What prophecies have yet to be fulfilled?

Peter Preaches in the Temple
Acts 3:12-25

12 Peter saw his opportunity and addressed the crowd. "People of Israel," he said, "what is so surprising about this? And why stare at us as though we had made this man walk by our own power or godliness? 13 For it is the God of Abraham, Isaac, and Jacob—the God of all our ancestors—who has brought glory to his servant Jesus by doing this. This is the same Jesus whom you handed over and rejected before Pilate, despite Pilate's decision to release him. 14 You rejected this holy, righteous one and instead demanded the release of a murderer. 15 You killed the author of life, but God raised him from the dead. And we are witnesses of this fact!

16 "Through faith in the name of Jesus, this man was healed—and you know how crippled he was before. Faith in Jesus' name has healed him before your very eyes.

17 "Friends, I realize that what you and your leaders did to Jesus was done in ignorance. 18 But God was fulfilling what all the prophets had foretold about the Messiah—that he must suffer these things. 19 Now repent of your sins and turn to God, so that your sins may be wiped away. 20 Then times of refreshment will come from the presence of the Lord, and he will again send you Jesus, your appointed Messiah. 21 For he must remain in heaven until the time for the final restoration of all things, as God promised long ago through his holy prophets. 22 Moses said, 'The Lord your God will raise up for you a Prophet like me from among your own people. Listen carefully to everything he tells you.' 23 Then Moses said, 'Anyone who will not listen to that Prophet will be completely cut off from God's people.'

24 "Starting with Samuel, every prophet spoke about what is happening today. 25 You are the children of those prophets, and you are included in the covenant God promised to your ancestors. For God said to Abraham, 'Through your descendants all the families on earth will be blessed.' 26 When God raised up his servant, Jesus, he sent him first to you people of Israel, to bless you by turning each of you back from your sinful ways."

Reflect.

The miraculous healing opened the door for Peter to preach a second sermon since the filling of the Holy Spirit on Pentecost.

Compare and contrast this sermon to the first sermon that he preached in Acts 2.

1. What is similar?

2. What is different?

3. What is the significance of what Peter says in verses 17-18?

4. What is significant about the fact that it was the religious leaders who took offense at the message of Peter? Does it surprise you? Why or why not?

Peter and John before the Council
Acts 4:1-22

While Peter and John were speaking to the people, they were confronted by the priests, the captain of the Temple guard, and some of the Sadducees. 2 These leaders were very disturbed that Peter and John were teaching the people that through Jesus there is a resurrection of the dead. 3 They arrested them and, since it was already evening, put them in jail until morning. 4 But many of the people who heard their message believed it, so the number of men who believed now totaled about 5,000.

5 The next day the council of all the rulers and elders and teachers of religious law met in Jerusalem. 6 Annas the high priest was there, along with Caiaphas, John, Alexander, and other relatives of the high priest. 7 They brought in the two disciples and demanded, "By what power, or in whose name, have you done this?"

8 Then Peter, filled with the Holy Spirit, said to them, "Rulers and elders of our people, 9 are we being questioned today because we've done a good deed for a crippled man? Do you want to know how he was healed? 10 Let me clearly state to all of you and to all the people of Israel that he was healed by the powerful name of Jesus Christ the Nazarene, the man you crucified but whom God raised from the dead. 11 For Jesus is the one referred to in the Scriptures, where it says,
'The stone that you builders rejected
  has now become the cornerstone.'
12 There is salvation in no one else! God has given no other name under heaven by which we must be saved."

13 The members of the council were amazed when they saw the boldness of Peter and John, for they could see that they were ordinary men with no special training in the Scriptures. They also recognized them as men who had been with Jesus. 14 But since they could see the man who had been healed standing right there among them, there was nothing the council could say. 15 So they ordered Peter and John out of the council chamber and conferred among themselves.

16 "What should we do with these men?" they asked each other. "We can't deny that they have performed a miraculous sign, and everybody in Jerusalem knows about it. 17 But to keep them from spreading their propaganda any further, we must warn them not to speak to anyone in Jesus' name again." 18 So they called the apostles back in and commanded them never again to speak or teach in the name of Jesus.

19 But Peter and John replied, "Do you think God wants us to obey you rather than him? 20 We cannot stop telling about everything we have seen and heard."

21 The council then threatened them further, but they finally let them go because they didn't know how to punish them without starting a riot. For everyone was praising God 22 for this miraculous sign—the healing of a man who had been lame for more than forty years.

Reflect.

1. Compare and contrast the significance of the statement made by Peter and John in verse 19 with the irony of the facts that are recorded in verses 21-22.

2. What is the application or lesson that you can learn and apply to your life?

The Believers Pray for Courage
Acts 4:23-31

23 As soon as they were freed, Peter and John returned to the other believers and told them what the leading priests and elders had said. 24 When they heard the report, all the believers lifted their voices together in prayer to God: "O Sovereign Lord, Creator of heaven and earth, the sea, and everything in them— 25 you spoke long ago by the Holy Spirit through our ancestor David, your servant, saying,
'Why were the nations so angry?
    Why did they waste their time with futile plans?
26 The kings of the earth prepared for battle;
  the rulers gathered together
against the Lord and against his Messiah.'
27 "In fact, this has happened here in this very city! For Herod Antipas, Pontius Pilate the governor, the Gentiles, and the people of Israel were all united against Jesus, your holy servant, whom you anointed. 28 But everything they did was determined beforehand according to your will. 29 And now, O Lord, hear their threats, and give us, your servants, great boldness in preaching your word. 30 Stretch out your hand with healing power; may miraculous signs and wonders be done through the name of your holy servant Jesus."
31 After this prayer, the meeting place shook, and they were all filled with the Holy Spirit. Then they preached the word of God with boldness.

Reflect.

After reading through the who passage go back and reflect on verse 26.

- In your own words describe the significance of the fact that the believers are recognizing that the attack was not against Peter and John but against the Messiah?

Read Ephesians 6:12, 18-19

1. How do these verses reflect the actions and the perspective of the disciples in Acts 4?

2. What can be learned and applied to your own life when you are experiencing similar attacks in your own life?

3. Application. What things in your life do you need to change your perspective about? Where are some areas where you have been attempting to "do battle" in your own power but need to change your battle plan and begin following the example and prayers of the of the believers in Acts 4 and the instructions of Paul in Ephesians 6?

The Believers Share Their Possessions
Acts 4:32-37

Reflect.

Community or Communism

Thoughts an questions for personal reflection and group dialogue:

Some people claim that the new community described in the book of Acts is really an example of communism.

1. What do you think?

2. What would be the similarities?

3. What would be the differences?

4. Why do you think that the believers in Acts behaved this way?

5. What was their motivation?

32 All the believers were united in heart and mind. And they felt that what they owned was not their own, so they shared everything they had. 33 The apostles testified powerfully to the resurrection of the Lord Jesus, and God's great blessing was upon them all. 34 There were no needy people among them, because those who owned land or houses would sell them 35 and bring the money to the apostles to give to those in need.

36 For instance, there was Joseph, the one the apostles nicknamed Barnabas (which means "Son of Encouragement"). He was from the tribe of Levi and came from the island of Cyprus. 37 He sold a field he owned and brought the money to the apostles.

6. What do you think is similar in your experience? What has been lost?

7. Should we still be acting this way today?

8. Should this be the normal experience?

9. Why or why not?

Ananias and Sapphira
Acts 5:1-11

But there was a certain man named Ananias who, with his wife, Sapphira, sold some property. 2 He brought part of the money to the apostles, claiming it was the full amount. With his wife's consent, he kept the rest.

3 Then Peter said, "Ananias, why have you let Satan fill your heart? You lied to the Holy Spirit, and you kept some of the money for yourself. 4 The property was yours to sell or not sell, as you wished. And after selling it, the money was also yours to give away. How could you do a thing like this? You weren't lying to us but to God!"

5 As soon as Ananias heard these words, he fell to the floor and died. Everyone who heard about it was terrified. 6 Then some young men got up, wrapped him in a sheet, and took him out and buried him.

7 About three hours later his wife came in, not knowing what had happened. 8 Peter asked her, "Was this the price you and your husband received for your land?"

"Yes," she replied, "that was the price."

9 And Peter said, "How could the two of you even think of conspiring to test the Spirit of the Lord like this? The young men who buried your husband are just outside the door, and they will carry you out, too."

10 Instantly, she fell to the floor and died. When the young men came in and saw that she was dead, they carried her out and buried her beside her husband. 11 Great fear gripped the entire church and everyone else who heard what had happened.

Reflect.

1. Compare and contrast these verses in chapter 5 with the way that chapter 4 finished. In some ways chapter 4 could be misinterpreted into having our generation believe that life was a utopia where everyone within the body of Christ had pure motivation and co-missioned together. But chapter 5 brings us back to the reality of sin, sinful people, and sinful motivation.

2. In your own words why do you think that this story is recorded in the book of Acts?

3. What is the application for you and I as we attempt to co-mission with Christ but are sometimes discouraged because of the "realities of religious people" in our own context?

The Apostles Heal Many
Acts 5:12-16

Reflect.

It would be an understatement to say that Peter and the apostles have come a long way in just 5 short chapters.

Yet there is something perplexing about the tension between verses 13 and 14.

On one hand people are scared to join them (presumably because of the possibility of persecution) while on the other hand there are numerous new believers).

1. What do you think is going to be the impact of this tension between maturing believers and a host of new younger believers on the culture of the church as a whole?

12 The apostles were performing many miraculous signs and wonders among the people. And all the believers were meeting regularly at the Temple in the area known as Solomon's Colonnade. 13 But no one else dared to join them, even though all the people had high regard for them. 14 Yet more and more people believed and were brought to the Lord—crowds of both men and women. 15 As a result of the apostles' work, sick people were brought out into the streets on beds and mats so that Peter's shadow might fall across some of them as he went by. 16 Crowds came from the villages around Jerusalem, bringing their sick and those possessed by evil spirits, and they were all healed.

2. Have you seen or experienced something similar in your church? If so, describe what happened?

3. How is or was the "problem" of a large number of new believers being added to the church in a short period of time addressed? Was the result positive? What positive principles could be learned and applied? What could be done differently?

4. Do you think that your church or the modern church as a whole is designed to deal with the "problem" of large quantities of new believers being added to the number of Christians within a short period of time? Why or why not?

5. What systems or methods of church would need to be changed or addressed to accommodate this type of "problem" and equip churches to disciple a large number of new believers?

The Apostles Meet Opposition
Acts 5:17-42

17 The high priest and his officials, who were Sadducees, were filled with jealousy. 18 They arrested the apostles and put them in the public jail. 19 But an angel of the Lord came at night, opened the gates of the jail, and brought them out. Then he told them, 20 "Go to the Temple and give the people this message of life!"

21 So at daybreak the apostles entered the Temple, as they were told, and immediately began teaching.

When the high priest and his officials arrived, they convened the high council—the full assembly of the elders of Israel. Then they sent for the apostles to be brought from the jail for trial. 22 But when the Temple guards went to the jail, the men were gone. So they returned to the council and reported, 23 "The jail was securely locked, with the guards standing outside, but when we opened the gates, no one was there!"

24 When the captain of the Temple guard and the leading priests heard this, they were perplexed, wondering where it would all end. 25 Then someone arrived with startling news: "The men you put in jail are standing in the Temple, teaching the people!"

26 The captain went with his Temple guards and arrested the apostles, but without violence, for they were afraid the people would stone them. 27 Then they brought the apostles before the high council, where the high priest confronted them. 28 "We gave you strict orders never again to teach in this man's name!" he said. "Instead, you have filled all Jerusalem with your teaching about him, and you want to make us responsible for his death!"

29 But Peter and the apostles replied, "We must obey God rather than any human authority. 30 The God of our ancestors raised Jesus from the dead after you killed him by hanging him on a cross. 31 Then God put him in the place of honor at his right hand as Prince and Savior. He did this so the people of Israel would repent of their sins and be forgiven. 32 We are witnesses of these things and so is the Holy Spirit, who is given by God to those who obey him."

33 When they heard this, the high council was furious and decided to kill them. 34 But one member, a Pharisee named Gamaliel, who was an expert in religious law and respected by all the people, stood up and ordered that the men be sent outside the council chamber for a while. 35 Then he said to his colleagues, "Men of Israel, take care what you are planning to do to these men! 36 Some time ago there was that fellow Theudas, who pretended to be someone great. About 400 others joined him, but he was killed, and all his followers went their various ways. The whole movement came to nothing. 37 After him, at the time of the census, there was Judas of Galilee. He got people to follow him, but he was killed, too, and all his followers were scattered.

38 "So my advice is, leave these men alone. Let them go. If they are planning and doing these things merely on their own, it will soon be overthrown. 39 But if it is from God, you will not be able to overthrow them. You may even find yourselves fighting against God!"

40 The others accepted his advice. They called in the apostles and had them flogged. Then they ordered them never again to speak in the name of Jesus, and they let them go.

41 The apostles left the high council rejoicing that God had counted them worthy to suffer disgrace for the name of Jesus. 42 And every day, in the Temple and from house to house, they continued to teach and preach this message: "Jesus is the Messiah."

Seven Men Chosen to Serve
Acts 6:1-7

But as the believers rapidly multiplied, there were rumblings of discontent. The Greek-speaking believers complained about the Hebrew-speaking believers, saying that their widows were being discriminated against in the daily distribution of food.
2 So the Twelve called a meeting of all the believers. They said, "We apostles should spend our time teaching the word of God, not running a food program. 3 And so, brothers, select seven men who are well respected and are full of the Spirit and wisdom. We will give them this responsibility.

4 Then we apostles can spend our time in prayer and teaching the word."
5 Everyone liked this idea, and they chose the following: Stephen (a man full of faith and the Holy Spirit), Philip, Procorus, Nicanor, Timon, Parmenas, and Nicolas of Antioch (an earlier convert to the Jewish faith). 6 These seven were presented to the apostles, who prayed for them as they laid their hands on them. 7 So God's message continued to spread. The number of believers greatly increased in Jerusalem, and many of the Jewish priests were converted, too.

Reflect.

1. What is the significance of that in verse 17 we are informed that the High Priest and the officials were "filled with jealousy"? What does that tell us about their motivation?

2. What could be the personal application for you in some of the conflict that you may experience in the midst of watching God at work in and through your life?

3. As you read through the rest of the passage what else do you find significant about the apostles, their message and their response to the religious leaders

4. What is significant about the description that the believers "rapidly multiplied" in Acts 6: 1?

5. There is a principle here between God at work, and the enemy of God attempting to thwart or derail God's work through conflict.

6. Read verse 7 and describe in your own words the significance of God's grace and the role of godly leadership in the outcome and result of the conflict.

Culture and Conflict

In the midst of the rapid multiplication and the addition of numerous new believers there arises conflict. What makes this conflict interesting is that it is a cultural conflict with an accusation of discrimination.

The solution that is proposed forms the leadership model for the church that is the basis for the elder and deacon model of church leadership.

Items for consideration and discussion:

A. What is the significance of the fact that the conflict included the accusation of discrimination? Why does that matter? What is the application for today regarding both the accusation and the way that it was handled?

B. What is the significance of the job description of an elder? What is the significance of the job description of a deacon?

C. 1 Timothy 3:1 states that those who set their heart on being an overseer desire a noble task; have you ever considered aspiring toward a leadership role in the future? Why or why not?

D. What steps should you begin to take to prepared yourself for that type of role and opportunity?

Stephen is Arrested
Acts 6:8-15

Reflect.

1. Do some research and look up the Synagogue of Freed Slaves. What was it? How does it play into the conflict that was occurring between the Greeks and Hebrew speaking Jews?

2. Given the fact that Stephen is most likely a Hellenistic speaking Jew what is his likely connection to this group of people?

3. What would have been particularly discouraging to Stephen as a result of this connection?

4. Have you ever experienced a time when you were falsely accused of something? How did you feel? What happened as a result?

8 Stephen, a man full of God's grace and power, performed amazing miracles and signs among the people. 9 But one day some men from the Synagogue of Freed Slaves, as it was called, started to debate with him. They were Jews from Cyrene, Alexandria, Cilicia, and the province of Asia. 10 None of them could stand against the wisdom and the Spirit with which Stephen spoke.

11 So they persuaded some men to lie about Stephen, saying, "We heard him blaspheme Moses, and even God." 12 This roused the people, the elders, and the teachers of religious law. So they arrested Stephen and brought him before the high council.

13 The lying witnesses said, "This man is always speaking against the holy Temple and against the law of Moses. 14 We have heard him say that this Jesus of Nazareth will destroy the Temple and change the customs Moses handed down to us."

15 At this point everyone in the high council stared at Stephen, because his face became as bright as an angel's.

5. Observe and pattern that is occurring here in chapter 6 and then consider the application for your life.

   a. Growth.
   b. Conflict
   c. Wise leadership address the conflict
   d. More growth
   e. More conflict
   f. Persecution

6. Sometimes it is easy to believe that when we are doing the right things with the right motives that and God is at work that we should experience less conflict and yet it would appear that the exact opposite is happening here in chapter 6. Is this news comforting or disconcerting to you? Explain your answer.

7. How could observing and understanding this pattern help you to make sense out of life as you seek to serve Christ?

Stephen Addresses the Council
Acts 7:1-60

Then the high priest asked Stephen, "Are these accusations true?"

2 This was Stephen's reply: "Brothers and fathers, listen to me. Our glorious God appeared to our ancestor Abraham in Mesopotamia before he settled in Haran. 3 God told him, 'Leave your native land and your relatives, and come into the land that I will show you.' 4 So Abraham left the land of the Chaldeans and lived in Haran until his father died. Then God brought him here to the land where you now live.

5 "But God gave him no inheritance here, not even one square foot of land. God did promise, however, that eventually the whole land would belong to Abraham and his descendants—even though he had no children yet. 6 God also told him that his descendants would live in a foreign land, where they would be oppressed as slaves for 400 years. 7 'But I will punish the nation that enslaves them,' God said, 'and in the end they will come out and worship me here in this place.'

8 "God also gave Abraham the covenant of circumcision at that time. So when Abraham became the father of Isaac, he circumcised him on the eighth day. And the practice was continued when Isaac became the father of Jacob, and when Jacob became the father of the twelve patriarchs of the Israelite nation.

9 "These patriarchs were jealous of their brother Joseph, and they sold him to be a slave in Egypt. But God was with him 10 and rescued him from all his troubles. And God gave him favor before Pharaoh, king of Egypt. God also gave Joseph unusual wisdom, so that Pharaoh appointed him governor over all of Egypt and put him in charge of the palace.

11 "But a famine came upon Egypt and Canaan. There was great misery, and our ancestors ran out of food. 12 Jacob heard that there was still grain in Egypt, so he sent his sons—our ancestors—to buy some. 13 The second time they went, Joseph revealed his identity to his brothers, and they were introduced to Pharaoh. 14 Then Joseph sent for his father, Jacob, and all his relatives to come to Egypt, seventy-five persons in all. 15 So Jacob went to Egypt. He died there, as did our ancestors. 16 Their bodies were taken to Shechem and buried in the tomb Abraham had bought for a certain price from Hamor's sons in Shechem.

17 "As the time drew near when God would fulfill his promise to Abraham, the number of our people in Egypt greatly increased. 18 But then a new king came to the throne of Egypt who knew nothing about Joseph. 19 This king exploited our people and oppressed them, forcing parents to abandon their newborn babies so they would die.

20 "At that time Moses was born—a beautiful child in God's eyes. His parents cared for him at home for three months. 21 When they had to abandon him, Pharaoh's daughter adopted him and raised him as her own son. 22 Moses was taught all the wisdom of the Egyptians, and he was powerful in both speech and action.

23 "One day when Moses was forty years old, he decided to visit his relatives, the people of Israel. 24 He saw an Egyptian mistreating an Israelite. So Moses came to the man's defense and avenged him, killing the Egyptian. 25 Moses assumed his fellow Israelites would realize that God had sent him to rescue them, but they didn't.

26 "The next day he visited them again and saw two men of Israel fighting. He tried to be a peacemaker. 'Men,' he said, 'you are brothers. Why are you fighting each other?'

Stephen Addresses the Council
Acts 7:1-60

27 "But the man in the wrong pushed Moses aside. 'Who made you a ruler and judge over us?' he asked. 28 'Are you going to kill me as you killed that Egyptian yesterday?' 29 When Moses heard that, he fled the country and lived as a foreigner in the land of Midian. There his two sons were born.

30 "Forty years later, in the desert near Mount Sinai, an angel appeared to Moses in the flame of a burning bush. 31 When Moses saw it, he was amazed at the sight. As he went to take a closer look, the voice of the Lord called out to him, 32 'I am the God of your ancestors–the God of Abraham, Isaac, and Jacob.' Moses shook with terror and did not dare to look.

33 "Then the Lord said to him, 'Take off your sandals, for you are standing on holy ground. 34 I have certainly seen the oppression of my people in Egypt. I have heard their groans and have come down to rescue them. Now go, for I am sending you back to Egypt.'

35 "So God sent back the same man his people had previously rejected when they demanded, 'Who made you a ruler and judge over us?' Through the angel who appeared to him in the burning bush, God sent Moses to be their ruler and savior. 36 And by means of many wonders and miraculous signs, he led them out of Egypt, through the Red Sea, and through the wilderness for forty years.

37 "Moses himself told the people of Israel, 'God will raise up for you a Prophet like me from among your own people.' 38 Moses was with our ancestors, the assembly of God's people in the wilderness, when the angel spoke to him at Mount Sinai. And there Moses received life-giving words to pass on to us.

39 "But our ancestors refused to listen to Moses. They rejected him and wanted to return to Egypt. 40 They told Aaron, 'Make us some gods who can lead us, for we don't know what has become of this Moses, who brought us out of Egypt.' 41 So they made an idol shaped like a calf, and they sacrificed to it and celebrated over this thing they had made. 42 Then God turned away from them and abandoned them to serve the stars of heaven as their gods! In the book of the prophets it is written, 'Was it to me you were bringing sacrifices and offerings during those forty years in the wilderness, Israel?

43 No, you carried your pagan gods–
the shrine of Molech,
the star of your god Rephan,
and the images you made to worship them.
So I will send you into exile
as far away as Babylon.'

44 "Our ancestors carried the Tabernacle with them through the wilderness. It was constructed according to the plan God had shown to Moses. 45 Years later, when Joshua led our ancestors in battle against the nations that God drove out of this land, the Tabernacle was taken with them into their new territory. And it stayed there until the time of King David.

46 "David found favor with God and asked for the privilege of building a permanent Temple for the God of Jacob. 47 But it was Solomon who actually built it. 48 However, the Most High doesn't live in temples made by human hands. As the prophet says,

49 'Heaven is my throne,
and the earth is my footstool.
Could you build me a temple as good as that?'
asks the Lord.
'Could you build me such a resting place?
50 Didn't my hands make both heaven and earth?'

Stephen Addresses the Council
Acts 7:1-60

51 "You stubborn people! You are heathen at heart and deaf to the truth. Must you forever resist the Holy Spirit? That's what your ancestors did, and so do you! 52 Name one prophet your ancestors didn't persecute! They even killed the ones who predicted the coming of the Righteous One–the Messiah whom you betrayed and murdered. 53 You deliberately disobeyed God's law, even though you received it from the hands of angels."
54 The Jewish leaders were infuriated by Stephen's accusation, and they shook their fists at him in rage.

55 But Stephen, full of the Holy Spirit, gazed steadily into heaven and saw the glory of God, and he saw Jesus standing in the place of honor at God's right hand.
56 And he told them, "Look, I see the heavens opened and the Son of Man standing in the place of honor at God's right hand!"
57 Then they put their hands over their ears and began shouting. They rushed at him 58 and dragged him out of the city and began to stone him. His accusers took off their coats and laid them at the feet of a young man named Saul.
59 As they stoned him, Stephen prayed, "Lord Jesus, receive my spirit." 60 He fell to his knees, shouting, "Lord, don't charge them with this sin!" And with that, he died.

Reflect.

1. Stephen was asked a fairly straightforward yes or no question and yet he launched into a sermon; why do you think he did that?

2. Stephen's sermon is now the third major sermon recorded in the book of Acts. Compare and contrast it with the first two. What is similar? What is different?

3. Toward the end of the message Stephen is fairly bold and incredibly blunt. This is definitely not a "seeker friendly" sermon where He promises his hearers that Jesus will make their life better by taking away their hardships and providing them a better life if they "just believe."

    •   How do you think that his unique audience of the descendants of freed Greek slaves impacted the way that he presented the gospel to them?

4. What is significance (and helpful) for us with the fact that Luke was sure to point out in verse 55 that Stephen was full of the Holy Spirit throughout this exchange?

5. Stephen's last words in verse 60 give us a reflection of his heart. The fact that he is asking God to forgive them helps us to see that his harsh words toward the religious leaders were not out of anger but with a sincere desire for them to repent. In our culture it is sometimes considered excusable (even noble) to not want to offend people with the Gospel.

6. But what is the balance between grace and truth? How do we live out the principle of 1Peter 3:15 of presenting the gospel with gentleness and respect while at the same time not being afraid under the leading of the Holy Spirit to confront people with their need to repent?

Persecution Scatters the Believers
Acts 8:1-3

Reflect.

A. What is significant about the words, "a great wave of persecution began that day, sweeping over the church?"

B. In your own words describe what it must have felt like to be a believer in Jerusalem right after the death of Stephen. What would your reaction have been to the "wave of persecution?" What would you expect to happen next?

Saul was one of the witnesses, and he agreed completely with the killing of Stephen.
A great wave of persecution began that day, sweeping over the church in Jerusalem; and all the believers except the apostles were scattered through the regions of Judea and Samaria. 2 (Some devout men came and buried Stephen with great mourning.) 3 But Saul was going everywhere to destroy the church. He went from house to house, dragging out both men and women to throw them into prison.

1. What is the significance of the mention of Saul here in this passage and at this particular point in church history?

2. Based on the description given in this passage how would you describe Saul?

3. Do a search on Saul and the descriptions given in other parts of the New Testament about his life prior to meeting Jesus Christ and then write up a full description of who he was and what he was like. Note the references that you use.

4. Based on your description of Saul what would your assessment have been of the likelihood of him becoming a follower of Christ let along a missionary for Christ? Explain your answer.

5. Who in your circles of influence currently feels like a Saul? What has been your current response to that person? Have you been judging them? Avoiding them? Praying for them? What has motivated you to take the current approach that you are taking? Explain your answer.

6. What would happen if you and your small group committed to pray for that person once each day for the remainder of the semester that God would reach them with the truth of His love and forgiveness in the same way that he reached the heart of Paul? Would you be willing to make that commitment with a small group of 2-3 friends? Talk it through and then take actions steps.

Philip Preaches in Samaria
Acts 8:4-25

4 But the believers who were scattered preached the Good News about Jesus wherever they went. 5 Philip, for example, went to the city of Samaria and told the people there about the Messiah. 6 Crowds listened intently to Philip because they were eager to hear his message and see the miraculous signs he did. 7 Many evil spirits were cast out, screaming as they left their victims. And many who had been paralyzed or lame were healed. 8 So there was great joy in that city.

9 A man named Simon had been a sorcerer there for many years, amazing the people of Samaria and claiming to be someone great. 10 Everyone, from the least to the greatest, often spoke of him as "the Great One—the Power of God." 11 They listened closely to him because for a long time he had astounded them with his magic.

12 But now the people believed Philip's message of Good News concerning the Kingdom of God and the name of Jesus Christ. As a result, many men and women were baptized. 13 Then Simon himself believed and was baptized. He began following Philip wherever he went, and he was amazed by the signs and great miracles Philip performed.

14 When the apostles in Jerusalem heard that the people of Samaria had accepted God's message, they sent Peter and John there. 15 As soon as they arrived, they prayed for these new believers to receive the Holy Spirit.

16 The Holy Spirit had not yet come upon any of them, for they had only been baptized in the name of the Lord Jesus. 17 Then Peter and John laid their hands upon these believers, and they received the Holy Spirit.

18 When Simon saw that the Spirit was given when the apostles laid their hands on people, he offered them money to buy this power. 19 "Let me have this power, too," he exclaimed, "so that when I lay my hands on people, they will receive the Holy Spirit!"

20 But Peter replied, "May your money be destroyed with you for thinking God's gift can be bought! 21 You can have no part in this, for your heart is not right with God. 22 Repent of your wickedness and pray to the Lord. Perhaps he will forgive your evil thoughts, 23 for I can see that you are full of bitter jealousy and are held captive by sin."

24 "Pray to the Lord for me," Simon exclaimed, "that these terrible things you've said won't happen to me!"

25 After testifying and preaching the word of the Lord in Samaria, Peter and John returned to Jerusalem. And they stopped in many Samaritan villages along the way to preach the Good News.

Reflect.

1. In light of the mission of God to fill the earth with His glory, what is the irony that persecution from the enemies of the gospel caused the church to scatter and the gospel message to spread? What is the application and what could be the expectation in our own lives?

2. Tell the story of Simon the sorcerer in your own words.

3. How would you disciple Simon? What spiritual needs does he have at each of the stages in his story?

Philip and the Ethiopian Eunuch
Acts 8:26-40

26 As for Philip, an angel of the Lord said to him, "Go south down the desert road that runs from Jerusalem to Gaza." 27 So he started out, and he met the treasurer of Ethiopia, a eunuch of great authority under the Kandake, the queen of Ethiopia. The eunuch had gone to Jerusalem to worship, 28 and he was now returning. Seated in his carriage, he was reading aloud from the book of the prophet Isaiah.
29 The Holy Spirit said to Philip, "Go over and walk along beside the carriage."
30 Philip ran over and heard the man reading from the prophet Isaiah. Philip asked, "Do you understand what you are reading?"
31 The man replied, "How can I, unless someone instructs me?" And he urged Philip to come up into the carriage and sit with him.

32 The passage of Scripture he had been reading was this:

"He was led like a sheep to the slaughter.
  And as a lamb is silent before the shearers,
  he did not open his mouth.
33 He was humiliated and received no justice.
  Who can speak of his descendants?
  For his life was taken from the earth."
34 The eunuch asked Philip, "Tell me, was the prophet talking about himself or someone else?" 35 So beginning with this same Scripture, Philip told him the Good News about Jesus.

36 As they rode along, they came to some water, and the eunuch said, "Look! There's some water! Why can't I be baptized?" 38 He ordered the carriage to stop, and they went down into the water, and Philip baptized him.

39 When they came up out of the water, the Spirit of the Lord snatched Philip away. The eunuch never saw him again but went on his way rejoicing. 40 Meanwhile, Philip found himself farther north at the town of Azotus. He preached the Good News there and in every town along the way until he came to Caesarea.

Reflect.

In Acts 1: 8 the disciples are promised that they will "receive power" when the Holy Spirit comes upon them.

It is impossible to read chapter 8 of the book of Acts without recognizing the incredibly overt role of the Holy Spirit leading, filling and guiding and empowering the believers and transforming the lives of people at every stage in their relationship with God.

The story of Philip and the Ethiopian is more of the same. Obviously there are some parts of this story that are supernatural in ways that are miraculous, but even the parts of the story that can be explained like the actual transformation of a heart are still miraculous.

1. Where in your cultural context do you see interaction and dependence upon the power of the Holy Spirit.

2. Is it something that is common? Explain your answer.

In the late 1800's the founder of The Salvation Army, General William Booth stated,

"The chief danger that confronts the coming century will be religion without the Holy Ghost, Christianity without Christ, forgiveness without repentance, salvation without regeneration, politics without God, heaven without hell."

3. How do you feel his words apply to our generation? Explain your answer.

4. Close your time today in prayer asking God to redirect His church (starting with yourself and other students involved in this curriculum) back to a dependence upon the Holy Spirit for our power to fulfill His mission through our generation.

Our Great Cloud
of Witnesses

Christ & Culture

Great Cloud of Witnesses Project & Presentation

History repeats itself if nobody listens

Who are the great cloud of witnesses that we can learn from?

Students will make a formal presentation on the life of a witness or the impact of a historical movement or event that is relevant to our modern interpretation and understanding of the relationship between Culture & Theology.

Students presentations will include a handcrafted visual aid but may not include a power point, keynote or slide deck presentation.

Students will submit a formal single page reflection of the life of their witness or the event that they have researched that will interact with the following questions.

The student presentation will be 4-7 minutes long. Research and Reflection on the seven questions must be evident through oral or visual communication during the presentation.

Part II. Questions for research and reflection

1. What was the cultural giant that the witness faced?

2. What was the Christ-centered solution proposed by the witness?

3. What was the cultural pressure that the witnessed faced?

4. How did the witness response to the opposition?

5. What events or circumstances in the life of the witness did God use to prepare the witness to face the giant?

6. Of the five perspectives; what approach toward Christ and culture did the witness opt for? Why?

7. What were the solutions proposed by some of the witnesses' contemporaries? What other options were tried and to what level of success or failure?

8. What made the response of this witness to the mission of God distinct, unique or noteworthy?

9. How did this witness reflect an integrated life? Did the witness finish well? Why or why not?

10. What could our generation learn from the life and approach of this witness?

Great Cloud of Witnesses Project & Presentation
History repeats itself if nobody listens

Who are some of the great cloud of witness that we can learn from?

1	Justin Martyer (c. 150)	28	Katherine von Bora (1499 - 1552
2	Irenaeus, Bishop of Lyons (c.170)	29	Matthew Henry (1662 -1714)
3	Tertullian (c. 196)	30	Jonathon Edwards (1703 - 1755)
4	Cyprian (c. 251)	31	Fanny Crosby (1820 - 1915)
5	Augustine of Hippo (c. 387)	32	J. Hudson Taylor (1883 - 1905)
6	Jerome (405)	33	The Student Volunteer Movement (c. 1886)
7	Saint Patrick (432)	34	Charles Finney (1792 – 1875)
8	Boniface (716)	35	Amy Carmichael (1867 – 1951)
9	Anselm, Archbishop of Canterbury (1093)	36	Corrie ten Boom (1892 – 1983)
10	John Wycliffe (c. 1380)	37	Elisabeth Elliot (1926 – June 15, 2015)
11	John Hus (1415)	38	William Carey (1761 – 1834)
12	Johann Gutenberg (1456)	39	Catherine Booth (1829 – 1890)
13	Michelangelo (1512)	40	William Booth (1829 – 1912)
14	Martin Luther (1517)	41	Charles Haddon Spurgeon (1834 – 1893)
15	Zwingli (1523)	42	Charles Wesley (
16	John Calvin (1536)	43	D.L. Moody (1837 – 1899)
17	Thomas Cranmer (1549)	44	Oswald Chamber (1874 – 1917)
18	John Knox (1559)	45	George Mueller
19	The King James Bible (1611)	46	Rembrandt (1662)
20	Isaac Watts (1707)	47	Robert Raikes (1780)
21	Adoniram Judson (1812)	48	Elizabeth Fry (1817)
22	Dietrich Bonhoeffer (1945	49	Saint Francis of Assisi (c. 1226)
23	Billy Graham (current)	50	Martin Luther King Jr. (1963)
24	Carol Cymbala (current)	51	Ruth Ruibal (current)
25	Anne Graham Lotz (current)	52	Mary Slessor (1848 – 1915)
26	David Brainerd (1718 – 1747)	53	David Livingstone (1813 – 1873)
27	Watchman Nee (1922)	54	Dawson Trotman (1933)

Great Cloud of Witnesses

History repeats itself if nobody listens

Name of the Witness _____ Dates

1   What was the cultural giant that the witness faced?

2   What was the Christ-centered solution proposed by the witness?

3   What was the cultural pressure that the witnessed faced?

4   How did the witness response to the opposition?

5   What events or circumstances in the life of the witness did God use to prepare the witness to face the giant?

6   Of the 5 perspectives; what approach toward Christ and culture did the witness opt for? Why?

7   What were the solutions proposed by some of the witnesses contemporaries?

8   What made the response of this witness to the mission of God distinct, unique or noteworthy?

9   How did this witness reflect an integrated life? Did the witness finish well? Why or why not?

10   What could our generation learn from the life and approach of this witness?

Crossing Cultures
The Conversion of Saul

Christ & Culture
INVITED TO GO &TEACH

Saul's Conversion
Acts 9:1-19

Meanwhile, Saul was uttering threats with every breath and was eager to kill the Lord's followers. So he went to the high priest. 2 He requested letters addressed to the synagogues in Damascus, asking for their cooperation in the arrest of any followers of the Way he found there. He wanted to bring them—both men and women—back to Jerusalem in chains.
3 As he was approaching Damascus on this mission, a light from heaven suddenly shone down around him. 4 He fell to the ground and heard a voice saying to him, "Saul! Saul! Why are you persecuting me?"
5 "Who are you, lord?" Saul asked.
And the voice replied, "I am Jesus, the one you are persecuting! 6 Now get up and go into the city, and you will be told what you must do."
7 The men with Saul stood speechless, for they heard the sound of someone's voice but saw no one! 8 Saul picked himself up off the ground, but when he opened his eyes he was blind. So his companions led him by the hand to Damascus. 9 He remained there blind for three days and did not eat or drink.
10 Now there was a believer in Damascus named Ananias. The Lord spoke to him in a vision, calling, "Ananias!"

"Yes, Lord!" he replied.
11 The Lord said, "Go over to Straight Street, to the house of Judas. When you get there, ask for a man from Tarsus named Saul. He is praying to me right now. 12 I have shown him a vision of a man named Ananias coming in and laying hands on him so he can see again."
13 "But Lord," exclaimed Ananias, "I've heard many people talk about the terrible things this man has done to the believers in Jerusalem! 14 And he is authorized by the leading priests to arrest everyone who calls upon your name."
15 But the Lord said, "Go, for Saul is my chosen instrument to take my message to the Gentiles and to kings, as well as to the people of Israel. 16 And I will show him how much he must suffer for my name's sake."
17 So Ananias went and found Saul. He laid his hands on him and said, "Brother Saul, the Lord Jesus, who appeared to you on the road, has sent me so that you might regain your sight and be filled with the Holy Spirit." 18 Instantly something like scales fell from Saul's eyes, and he regained his sight. Then he got up and was baptized. 19 Afterward he ate some food and regained his strength.

Reflect

We have already written a profile on Saul but the description in verse 1 of chapter 9 is still fairly amazing. Saul appears almost blood thirsty. He is a man of death who is "eager to kill" and yet God without apology intervenes and chooses to reveal Himself to Saul in a dramatic way.

It is easy in a world of video games, comic book movies and fantasy novels to almost trivialize the story of Saul's encounter with the living God on the road to Damascus instead of meditating on the significance of it as a real historical event. As you read the story keep track of your emotions and your questions. Write them down and then share them together with your group.

After you are done sharing your thoughts as stores as a group consider carefully the rather ominous promise of God to Ananias in verse 16. What are your thoughts and reactions to that verse coming from God? How does it make you feel? Why?

Remember to close your time in prayer for the Saul's in your circles of influence. Don't give up or pray half-heartedly. Truly invite God to demonstrate His love and reveal Himself to those on your list.

Saul in Damascus and Jerusalem
Acts 9:19-31

Saul stayed with the believers in Damascus for a few days. 20 And immediately he began preaching about Jesus in the synagogues, saying, "He is indeed the Son of God!"

21 All who heard him were amazed. "Isn't this the same man who caused such devastation among Jesus' followers in Jerusalem?" they asked. "And didn't he come here to arrest them and take them in chains to the leading priests?"

22 Saul's preaching became more and more powerful, and the Jews in Damascus couldn't refute his proofs that Jesus was indeed the Messiah. 23 After a while some of the Jews plotted together to kill him. 24 They were watching for him day and night at the city gate so they could murder him, but Saul was told about their plot. 25 So during the night, some of the other believers lowered him in a large basket through an opening in the city wall.

26 When Saul arrived in Jerusalem, he tried to meet with the believers, but they were all afraid of him. They did not believe he had truly become a believer! 27 Then Barnabas brought him to the apostles and told them how Saul had seen the Lord on the way to Damascus and how the Lord had spoken to Saul. He also told them that Saul had preached boldly in the name of Jesus in Damascus.

28 So Saul stayed with the apostles and went all around Jerusalem with them, preaching boldly in the name of the Lord. 29 He debated with some Greek-speaking Jews, but they tried to murder him. 30 When the believers heard about this, they took him down to Caesarea and sent him away to Tarsus, his hometown.
31 The church then had peace throughout Judea, Galilee, and Samaria, and it became stronger as the believers lived in the fear of the Lord. And with the encouragement of the Holy Spirit, it also grew in numbers.

Reflect.

1. Put yourself in the shoes of the Damascus believers. How would you have felt if Saul would have shown up preaching in your synagogue?

   Consider the level of spiritual maturity for those who risked their lives to save Him. At this point in the story things might feel a bit like a movie script with persecution, scattering believers, miraculous transformations but one thing remains the same; a complete dependence upon the Spirit of God.

2. Read verse 31 together as a small group and then use that verse as an outline for a time of prayer together. Ask God to grant peace to those believers who live in fear of the Lord.

3. Ask the Holy Spirit to encourage believers to grow stronger in Him as they grow more dependent upon Him. And ask the Lord to bring more glory to His name by bringing a greater number of people to the saving knowledge of Him and His Son Jesus Christ.

4. As you pray, consider praying for the other Christian school students around the world who are using this same curriculum. Ask God to raise up an army of Christ-followers in your generation who are committed to be dependent upon the power of the Holy Spirit to fulfill His mission in their lives.

5. Ask God to give you the boldness of Saul in verse 28 and the steadfastness to persevere and not quit in the face of persecution (verse 29-30).

Peter Heals Aeneas, Raises Dorcas and meets Cornelius
Acts 9:32-43, 10:1-16

32 Meanwhile, Peter traveled from place to place, and he came down to visit the believers in the town of Lydda. 33 There he met a man named Aeneas, who had been paralyzed and bedridden for eight years. 34 Peter said to him, "Aeneas, Jesus Christ heals you! Get up, and roll up your sleeping mat!" And he was healed instantly. 35 Then the whole population of Lydda and Sharon saw Aeneas walking around, and they turned to the Lord.

36 There was a believer in Joppa named Tabitha (which in Greek is Dorcas). She was always doing kind things for others and helping the poor. 37 About this time she became ill and died. Her body was washed for burial and laid in an upstairs room. 38 But the believers had heard that Peter was nearby at Lydda, so they sent two men to beg him, "Please come as soon as possible!"

39 So Peter returned with them; and as soon as he arrived, they took him to the upstairs room. The room was filled with widows who were weeping and showing him the coats and other clothes Dorcas had made for them. 40 But Peter asked them all to leave the room; then he knelt and prayed. Turning to the body he said, "Get up, Tabitha." And she opened her eyes! When she saw Peter, she sat up! 41 He gave her his hand and helped her up. Then he called in the widows and all the believers, and he presented her to them alive.

42 The news spread through the whole town, and many believed in the Lord. 43 And Peter stayed a long time in Joppa, living with Simon, a tanner of hides.

In Caesarea there lived a Roman army officer named Cornelius, who was a captain of the Italian Regiment. 2 He was a devout, God-fearing man, as was everyone in his household. He gave generously to the poor and prayed regularly to God.

3 One afternoon about three o'clock, he had a vision in which he saw an angel of God coming toward him. "Cornelius!" the angel said.

4 Cornelius stared at him in terror. "What is it, sir?" he asked the angel.

And the angel replied, "Your prayers and gifts to the poor have been received by God as an offering! 5 Now send some men to Joppa, and summon a man named Simon Peter. 6 He is staying with Simon, a tanner who lives near the seashore."

7 As soon as the angel was gone, Cornelius called two of his household servants and a devout soldier, one of his personal attendants. 8 He told them what had happened and sent them off to Joppa.

9 The next day as Cornelius's messengers were nearing the town, Peter went up on the flat roof to pray. It was about noon, 10 and he was hungry. But while a meal was being prepared, he fell into a trance. 11 He saw the sky open, and something like a large sheet was let down by its four corners. 12 In the sheet were all sorts of animals, reptiles, and birds. 13 Then a voice said to him, "Get up, Peter; kill and eat them."
14 "No, Lord," Peter declared. "I have never eaten anything that our Jewish laws have declared impure and unclean."

15 But the voice spoke again: "Do not call something unclean if God has made it clean." 16 The same vision was repeated three times. Then the sheet was suddenly pulled up to heaven.

17 Peter was very perplexed. What could the vision mean? Just then the men sent by Cornelius found Simon's house. Standing outside the gate, 18 they asked if a man named Simon Peter was staying there.

Peter Visits Cornelius
Acts 10:17-48

19 Meanwhile, as Peter was puzzling over the vision, the Holy Spirit said to him, "Three men have come looking for you. 20 Get up, go downstairs, and go with them without hesitation. Don't worry, for I have sent them."

21 So Peter went down and said, "I'm the man you are looking for. Why have you come?"

22 They said, "We were sent by Cornelius, a Roman officer. He is a devout and God-fearing man, well respected by all the Jews. A holy angel instructed him to summon you to his house so that he can hear your message." 23 So Peter invited the men to stay for the night. The next day he went with them, accompanied by some of the brothers from Joppa.

24 They arrived in Caesarea the following day. Cornelius was waiting for them and had called together his relatives and close friends. 25 As Peter entered his home, Cornelius fell at his feet and worshiped him. 26 But Peter pulled him up and said, "Stand up! I'm a human being just like you!" 27 So they talked together and went inside, where many others were assembled.

28 Peter told them, "You know it is against our laws for a Jewish man to enter a Gentile home like this or to associate with you. But God has shown me that I should no longer think of anyone as impure or unclean. 29 So I came without objection as soon as I was sent for. Now tell me why you sent for me."

30 Cornelius replied, "Four days ago I was praying in my house about this same time, three o'clock in the afternoon. Suddenly, a man in dazzling clothes was standing in front of me. 31 He told me, 'Cornelius, your prayer has been heard, and your gifts to the poor have been noticed by God!

32 Now send messengers to Joppa, and summon a man named Simon Peter. He is staying in the home of Simon, a tanner who lives near the seashore.'

33 So I sent for you at once, and it was good of you to come. Now we are all here, waiting before God to hear the message the Lord has given you."

34 Then Peter replied, "I see very clearly that God shows no favoritism. 35 In every nation he accepts those who fear him and do what is right. 36 This is the message of Good News for the people of Israel–that there is peace with God through Jesus Christ, who is Lord of all. 37 You know what happened throughout Judea, beginning in Galilee, after John began preaching his message of baptism. 38 And you know that God anointed Jesus of Nazareth with the Holy Spirit and with power. Then Jesus went around doing good and healing all who were oppressed by the devil, for God was with him.

39 "And we apostles are witnesses of all he did throughout Judea and in Jerusalem. They put him to death by hanging him on a cross, 40 but God raised him to life on the third day. Then God allowed him to appear, 41 not to the general public, but to us whom God had chosen in advance to be his witnesses. We were those who ate and drank with him after he rose from the dead. 42 And he ordered us to preach everywhere and to testify that Jesus is the one appointed by God to be the judge of all–the living and the dead. 43 He is the one all the prophets testified about, saying that everyone who believes in him will have their sins forgiven through his name."

44 Even as Peter was saying these things, the Holy Spirit fell upon all who were listening to the message.

45 The Jewish believers who came with Peter were amazed that the gift of the Holy Spirit had been poured out on the Gentiles, too. 46 For they heard them speaking in other tongues and praising God.

Then Peter asked, 47 "Can anyone object to their being baptized, now that they have received the Holy Spirit just as we did?" 48 So he gave orders for them to be baptized in the name of Jesus Christ. Afterward Cornelius asked him to stay with them for several days.

The Gentiles Hear the Good News
Acts 9:32-43, 10:1-48

Study the passage for yourself and then write a Bible Study on Act 9:32, 10:1-48.

   a. What is the main point or principle of the passage?

   b. What are the specific applications of this passage to a class on Christ and Culture? What are the cultural issues that are being raised? What are the cultural issues that are being challenge? Why are they significant? How do they apply to our current culture?

   c. How would you teach these principles to someone else?

   d. What questions would you ask?

   e. What is the application that you would want to challenge them to make?

   f. Write out your study believe and then be prepared to lead someone through your study during a future class period.

Peter Explains His Actions
Acts 11:1-18

Soon the news reached the apostles and other believers in Judea that the Gentiles had received the word of God. 2 But when Peter arrived back in Jerusalem, the Jewish believers criticized him. 3 "You entered the home of Gentiles and even ate with them!" they said.

4 Then Peter told them exactly what had happened. 5 "I was in the town of Joppa," he said, "and while I was praying, I went into a trance and saw a vision. Something like a large sheet was let down by its four corners from the sky. And it came right down to me. 6 When I looked inside the sheet, I saw all sorts of tame and wild animals, reptiles, and birds. 7 And I heard a voice say, 'Get up, Peter; kill and eat them.'

8 "'No, Lord,' I replied. 'I have never eaten anything that our Jewish laws have declared impure or unclean.'

9 "But the voice from heaven spoke again: 'Do not call something unclean if God has made it clean.' 10 This happened three times before the sheet and all it contained was pulled back up to heaven.

11 "Just then three men who had been sent from Caesarea arrived at the house where we were staying. 12 The Holy Spirit told me to go with them and not to worry that they were Gentiles. These six brothers here accompanied me, and we soon entered the home of the man who had sent for us. 13 He told us how an angel had appeared to him in his home and had told him, 'Send messengers to Joppa, and summon a man named Simon Peter. 14 He will tell you how you and everyone in your household can be saved!'

15 "As I began to speak," Peter continued, "the Holy Spirit fell on them, just as he fell on us at the beginning. 16 Then I thought of the Lord's words when he said, 'John baptized with water, but you will be baptized with the Holy Spirit.' 17 And since God gave these Gentiles the same gift he gave us when we believed in the Lord Jesus Christ, who was I to stand in God's way?"

18 When the others heard this, they stopped objecting and began praising God. They said, "We can see that God has also given the Gentiles the privilege of repenting of their sins and receiving eternal life."

Study the passage for yourself and then write a Bible Study on Acts 11:1-18

a. What is the main point or principle of the passage?

b. What are the specific applications of this passage to a class on Christ and Culture? What are the cultural issues that are being raised? What are the cultural issues that are being challenge? Why are they significant? How do they apply to our current culture?

c. How would you teach these principles to someone else?

d. What questions would you ask?

e. What is the application that you would want to challenge them to make?

f. Write out your study believe and then be prepared to lead someone through your study during a future class period.

The Church of Antioch and Syria
Acts 11:19-30

19 Meanwhile, the believers who had been scattered during the persecution after Stephen's death traveled as far as Phoenicia, Cyprus, and Antioch of Syria. They preached the word of God, but only to Jews.

20 However, some of the believers who went to Antioch from Cyprus and Cyrene began preaching to the Gentiles about the Lord Jesus. 21 The power of the Lord was with them, and a large number of these Gentiles believed and turned to the Lord.

22 When the church at Jerusalem heard what had happened, they sent Barnabas to Antioch. 23 When he arrived and saw this evidence of God's blessing, he was filled with joy, and he encouraged the believers to stay true to the Lord. 24 Barnabas was a good man, full of the Holy Spirit and strong in faith. And many people were brought to the Lord.
25 Then Barnabas went on to Tarsus to look for Saul. 26 When he found him, he brought him back to Antioch. Both of them stayed there with the church for a full year, teaching large crowds of people. (It was at Antioch that the believers were first called Christians.)

27 During this time some prophets traveled from Jerusalem to Antioch. 28 One of them named Agabus stood up in one of the meetings and predicted by the Spirit that a great famine was coming upon the entire Roman world. (This was fulfilled during the reign of Claudius.) 29 So the believers in Antioch decided to send relief to the brothers and sisters in Judea, everyone giving as much as they could. 30 This they did, entrusting their gifts to Barnabas and Saul to take to the elders of the church in Jerusalem.

Study the passage for yourself and then write a Bible Study on Act 11:19-30

a. What is the main point or principle of the passage?

b. What are the specific applications of this passage to a class on Christ and Culture? What are the cultural issues that are being raised? What are the cultural issues that are being challenge? Why are they significant? How do they apply to our current culture?

c. How would you teach these principles to someone else?

d. What questions would you ask?

e. What is the application that you would want to challenge them to make?

f. Write out your study believe and then be prepared to lead someone through your study during a future class period.

James is Killed and Peter is Imprisoned
Acts 12:1-19

About that time King Herod Agrippa began to persecute some believers in the church. 2 He had the apostle James (John's brother) killed with a sword. 3 When Herod saw how much this pleased the Jewish people, he also arrested Peter. (This took place during the Passover celebration.) 4 Then he imprisoned him, placing him under the guard of four squads of four soldiers each. Herod intended to bring Peter out for public trial after the Passover. 5 But while Peter was in prison, the church prayed very earnestly for him.

6 The night before Peter was to be placed on trial, he was asleep, fastened with two chains between two soldiers. Others stood guard at the prison gate. 7 Suddenly, there was a bright light in the cell, and an angel of the Lord stood before Peter. The angel struck him on the side to awaken him and said, "Quick! Get up!" And the chains fell off his wrists. 8 Then the angel told him, "Get dressed and put on your sandals." And he did. "Now put on your coat and follow me," the angel ordered.

9 So Peter left the cell, following the angel. But all the time he thought it was a vision. He didn't realize it was actually happening. 10 They passed the first and second guard posts and came to the iron gate leading to the city, and this opened for them all by itself. So they passed through and started walking down the street, and then the angel suddenly left him.

11 Peter finally came to his senses. "It's really true!" he said. "The Lord has sent his angel and saved me from Herod and from what the Jewish leaders had planned to do to me!"

12 When he realized this, he went to the home of Mary, the mother of John Mark, where many were gathered for prayer. 13 He knocked at the door in the gate, and a servant girl named Rhoda came to open it. 14 When she recognized Peter's voice, she was so overjoyed that, instead of opening the door, she ran back inside and told everyone, "Peter is standing at the door!"

15 "You're out of your mind!" they said. When she insisted, they decided, "It must be his angel."

16 Meanwhile, Peter continued knocking. When they finally opened the door and saw him, they were amazed. 17 He motioned for them to quiet down and told them how the Lord had led him out of prison. "Tell James and the other brothers what happened," he said. And then he went to another place.

18 At dawn there was a great commotion among the soldiers about what had happened to Peter. 19 Herod Agrippa ordered a thorough search for him. When he couldn't be found, Herod interrogated the guards and sentenced them to death. Afterward Herod left Judea to stay in Caesarea for a while.

Peter's Miraculous Escape from Prison
Acts 12:1-19

Study the passage for yourself and then write a Bible Study on Act 9:32, 10:1-48.

    a.   What is the main point or principle of the passage?

    b.   What are the specific applications of this passage to a class on Christ and Culture? What are the cultural issues that are being raised? What are the cultural issues that are being challenge? Why are they significant? How do they apply to our current culture?

    c.   How would you teach these principles to someone else?

    d.   What questions would you ask?

    e.   What is the application that you would want to challenge them to make?

    f.   Write out your study believe and then be prepared to lead someone through your study during a future class period.

The Death of Herod Agrippa
Acts 12:20-25

20 Now Herod was very angry with the people of Tyre and Sidon. So they sent a delegation to make peace with him because their cities were dependent upon Herod's country for food. The delegates won the support of Blastus, Herod's personal assistant, 21 and an appointment with Herod was granted. When the day arrived, Herod put on his royal robes, sat on his throne, and made a speech to them. 22 The people gave him a great ovation, shouting, "It's the voice of a god, not of a man!"

23 Instantly, an angel of the Lord struck Herod with a sickness, because he accepted the people's worship instead of giving the glory to God. So he was consumed with worms and died.

24 Meanwhile, the word of God continued to spread, and there were many new believers.

25 When Barnabas and Saul had finished their mission to Jerusalem, they returned, taking John Mark with them.

Respond.

Reflect.

Barnabas and Saul Are Commissioned
Acts 13:1-3

Among the prophets and teachers of the church at Antioch of Syria were Barnabas, Simeon (called "the black man"), Lucius (from Cyrene), Manaen (the childhood companion of King Herod Antipas), and Saul. 2 One day as these men were worshiping the Lord and fasting, the Holy Spirit said, "Appoint Barnabas and Saul for the special work to which I have called them." 3 So after more fasting and prayer, the men laid their hands on them and sent them on their way.

Reflect.

At first glance this seems like a relatively short passage that might merely act as a transition between major parts of the Acts storyline, but in fact these three verses are significant on multiple levels.

First, we are now reading about a mature church.

For quite awhile the church has been working through some fairly significant growing pains. Conflict among new believers, persecution, prejudice and discrimination just to name a few of the major items that have been considered a normal part of life.

But now we have the "church" meeting in Antioch being led by a group of "prophets and teachers" meaning that there is evidence of spiritually mature people serving in biblical offices side by side. This is significant in and of itself on many levels.

Today we often have Pastors in the pulpit exercising a prophetic gift of forth telling or proclaiming the scriptures and we have teachers of the Bible who teach in Christian schools but seldom do we see these two offices filled with spiritually mature leaders who value both offices and work side by side.

In addition to an intentional diversity among the spiritual offices we also have an intentional diversity in nationality among the leadership team.

But not only do we see an illustration of spiritual maturity through diversity we also get a sense of spiritual maturity in their practice of worship, fasting and the intentionality by which they are listening to the Holy Spirit.

What is perhaps one of the largest indicators of the level of spiritual maturity among this group of church leaders is that when the Holy Spirit speaks to them in the midst of their fasting and prayer they do not immediately stop fasting and act with the reckless or rash impetuousness that is often a marker of youthful exuberance.

Instead, they continue to fast and pray and then ultimately lay their hands on Saul and Barnabas in an act of faithful obedience.

There is a lot to contemplate and a lot to apply from this description of Godly leadership.

As you meditate on this passage ask God to reveal His heart to you through the words of Scripture. What is He inviting you to see and apply to your own life?

Write it down in devotional reflection and then share it with those in your group.

Paul's First Missionary Journey
Acts 13-14

The First Missionary Journey of Paul

Study the first missionary journey of Paul and prepare a formal presentation.

Where did he go? What happened? What patterns emerge from the process of what happened? Patterns of persecution; patterns of the Spirit of God at work; patterns of salvation. What principles can be applied? How would you teach this to someone else?

Your assignment is to make a presentation of the first missionary journey of Paul that demonstrates personal understanding and teaches the content in a meaningful and engaging way. You can be creative and use media or any form of audio/visual communication. You can also work in a team, but each member of your team must demonstrate full participation in the final presentation and must turn-in notes from their study of the passage.

For each member of your team, you are allowed one minute of content presentation. Be wise in the number of people who are in your group. If you choose too large a group, then it may be difficult to keep everyone involved, and your presentation may run so long that it is less than engaging. If you choose too small of a group, then you will have difficulty presenting all of the various parts of the content in the amount of time.

Hint: Have your entire group study the whole passage individually first and then assign different sections to different people for the actual presentation. Then work together to find the common themes and common patterns that outline the entire journey. Finally put together a cohesive script. Film each part of the presentation and then edit it together into one larger presentation that meets the time constraints.

4 So Barnabas and Saul were sent out by the Holy Spirit. They went down to the seaport of Seleucia and then sailed for the island of Cyprus. 5 There, in the town of Salamis, they went to the Jewish synagogues and preached the word of God. John Mark went with them as their assistant.

6 Afterward they traveled from town to town across the entire island until finally they reached Paphos, where they met a Jewish sorcerer, a false prophet named Bar-Jesus. 7 He had attached himself to the governor, Sergius Paulus, who was an intelligent man. The governor invited Barnabas and Saul to visit him, for he wanted to hear the word of God. 8 But Elymas, the sorcerer (as his name means in Greek), interfered and urged the governor to pay no attention to what Barnabas and Saul said. He was trying to keep the governor from believing.

9 Saul, also known as Paul, was filled with the Holy Spirit, and he looked the sorcerer in the eye. 10 Then he said, "You son of the devil, full of every sort of deceit and fraud, and enemy of all that is good! Will you never stop perverting the true ways of the Lord? 11 Watch now, for the Lord has laid his hand of punishment upon you, and you will be struck blind. You will not see the sunlight for some time." Instantly mist and darkness came over the man's eyes, and he began groping around begging for someone to take his hand and lead him.

12 When the governor saw what had happened, he became a believer, for he was astonished at the teaching about the Lord.

Paul Preaches in Antioch of Pisidia (the journey continues)
Acts 13:13-42

13 Paul and his companions then left Paphos by ship for Pamphylia, landing at the port town of Perga. There John Mark left them and returned to Jerusalem. 14 But Paul and Barnabas traveled inland to Antioch of Pisidia. On the Sabbath they went to the synagogue for the services. 15 After the usual readings from the books of Moses and the prophets, those in charge of the service sent them this message: "Brothers, if you have any word of encouragement for the people, come and give it."

16 So Paul stood, lifted his hand to quiet them, and started speaking. "Men of Israel," he said, "and you God-fearing Gentiles, listen to me.

17 "The God of this nation of Israel chose our ancestors and made them multiply and grow strong during their stay in Egypt. Then with a powerful arm he led them out of their slavery. 18 He put up with them through forty years of wandering in the wilderness. 19 Then he destroyed seven nations in Canaan and gave their land to Israel as an inheritance. 20 All this took about 450 years.

"After that, God gave them judges to rule until the time of Samuel the prophet. 21 Then the people begged for a king, and God gave them Saul son of Kish, a man of the tribe of Benjamin, who reigned for forty years. 22 But God removed Saul and replaced him with David, a man about whom God said, 'I have found David son of Jesse, a man after my own heart. He will do everything I want him to do.'

23 "And it is one of King David's descendants, Jesus, who is God's promised Savior of Israel! 24 Before he came, John the Baptist preached that all the people of Israel needed to repent of their sins and turn to God and be baptized. 25 As John was finishing his ministry he asked, 'Do you think I am the Messiah? No, I am not! But he is coming soon—and I'm not even worthy to be his slave and untie the sandals on his feet.'

26 "Brothers—you sons of Abraham, and also you God-fearing Gentiles—this message of salvation has been sent to us! 27 The people in Jerusalem and their leaders did not recognize Jesus as the one the prophets had spoken about.

Instead, they condemned him, and in doing this they fulfilled the prophets' words that are read every Sabbath. 28 They found no legal reason to execute him, but they asked Pilate to have him killed anyway.

29 "When they had done all that the prophecies said about him, they took him down from the cross and placed him in a tomb. 30 But God raised him from the dead! 31 And over a period of many days he appeared to those who had gone with him from Galilee to Jerusalem. They are now his witnesses to the people of Israel.

32 "And now we are here to bring you this Good News. The promise was made to our ancestors, 33 and God has now fulfilled it for us, their descendants, by raising Jesus. This is what the second psalm says about Jesus: 'You are my Son.

Today I have become your Father.'
34 For God had promised to raise him from the dead, not leaving him to rot in the grave. He said, 'I will give you the sacred blessings I promised to David.' 35 Another psalm explains it more fully: 'You will not allow your Holy One to rot in the grave.' 36 This is not a reference to David, for after David had done the will of God in his own generation, he died and was buried with his ancestors, and his body decayed. 37 No, it was a reference to someone else—someone whom God raised and whose body did not decay.

38 "Brothers, listen! We are here to proclaim that through this man Jesus there is forgiveness for your sins. 39 Everyone who believes in him is made right in God's sight—something the law of Moses could never do. 40 Be careful! Don't let the prophets' words apply to you. For they said,

41 'Look, you mockers,
  be amazed and die!
For I am doing something in your own day,
  something you wouldn't believe
  even if someone told you about it.'"

Paul Turns to the Gentiles (the journey continues)
Acts 13:44-52

42 As Paul and Barnabas left the synagogue that day, the people begged them to speak about these things again the next week. 43 Many Jews and devout converts to Judaism followed Paul and Barnabas, and the two men urged them to continue to rely on the grace of God.

44 The following week almost the entire city turned out to hear them preach the word of the Lord. 45 But when some of the Jews saw the crowds, they were jealous; so they slandered Paul and argued against whatever he said.

46 Then Paul and Barnabas spoke out boldly and declared, "It was necessary that we first preach the word of God to you Jews. But since you have rejected it and judged yourselves unworthy of eternal life, we will offer it to the Gentiles. 47 For the Lord gave us this command when he said,

'I have made you a light to the Gentiles,

to bring salvation to the farthest corners of the earth.'"

48 When the Gentiles heard this, they were very glad and thanked the Lord for his message; and all who were chosen for eternal life became believers. 49 So the Lord's message spread throughout that region.

Respond.

50 Then the Jews stirred up the influential religious women and the leaders of the city, and they incited a mob against Paul and Barnabas and ran them out of town. 51 So they shook the dust from their feet as a sign of rejection and went to the town of Iconium. 52 And the believers were filled with joy and with the Holy Spirit.

The same thing happened in Iconium. Paul and Barnabas went to the Jewish synagogue and preached with such power that a great number of both Jews and Greeks became believers. 2 Some of the Jews, however, spurned God's message and poisoned the minds of the Gentiles against Paul and Barnabas. 3 But the apostles stayed there a long time, preaching boldly about the grace of the Lord. And the Lord proved their message was true by giving them power to do miraculous signs and wonders. 4 But the people of the town were divided in their opinion about them. Some sided with the Jews, and some with the apostles.

5 Then a mob of Gentiles and Jews, along with their leaders, decided to attack and stone them. 6 When the apostles learned of it, they fled to the region of Lycaonia—to the towns of Lystra and Derbe and the surrounding area. 7 And there they preached the Good News.

Reflect.

Paul and Barnabas in Lystra and Derbe (the journey continues)
Acts 14:8-20

8 While they were at Lystra, Paul and Barnabas came upon a man with crippled feet. He had been that way from birth, so he had never walked. He was sitting 9 and listening as Paul preached. Looking straight at him, Paul realized he had faith to be healed. 10 So Paul called to him in a loud voice, "Stand up!" And the man jumped to his feet and started walking.

11 When the crowd saw what Paul had done, they shouted in their local dialect, "These men are gods in human form!" 12 They decided that Barnabas was the Greek god Zeus and that Paul was Hermes, since he was the chief speaker. 13 Now the temple of Zeus was located just outside the town. So the priest of the temple and the crowd brought bulls and wreaths of flowers to the town gates, and they prepared to offer sacrifices to the apostles.

14 But when the apostles Barnabas and Paul heard what was happening, they tore their clothing in dismay and ran out among the people, shouting, 15 "Friends, why are you doing this? We are merely human beings—just like you! We have come to bring you the Good News that you should turn from these worthless things and turn to the living God, who made heaven and earth, the sea, and everything in them. 16 In the past he permitted all the nations to go their own ways, 17 but he never left them without evidence of himself and his goodness. For instance, he sends you rain and good crops and gives you food and joyful hearts." 18 But even with these words, Paul and Barnabas could scarcely restrain the people from sacrificing to them.

19 Then some Jews arrived from Antioch and Iconium and won the crowds to their side. They stoned Paul and dragged him out of town, thinking he was dead. 20 But as the believers gathered around him, he got up and went back into the town. The next day he left with Barnabas for Derbe.

21 After preaching the Good News in Derbe and making many disciples, Paul and Barnabas returned to Lystra, Iconium, and Antioch of Pisidia, 22 where they strengthened the believers. They encouraged them to continue in the faith, reminding them that we must suffer many hardships to enter the Kingdom of God. 23 Paul and Barnabas also appointed elders in every church. With prayer and fasting, they turned the elders over to the care of the Lord, in whom they had put their trust. 24 Then they traveled back through Pisidia to Pamphylia. 25 They preached the word in Perga, then went down to Attalia.

26 Finally, they returned by ship to Antioch of Syria, where their journey had begun. The believers there had entrusted them to the grace of God to do the work they had now completed. 27 Upon arriving in Antioch, they called the church together and reported everything God had done through them and how he had opened the door of faith to the Gentiles, too. 28 And they stayed there with the believers for a long time.

Respond.

Reflect.

The Council at Jerusalem
Acts 15:1-21

While Paul and Barnabas were at Antioch of Syria, some men from Judea arrived and began to teach the believers: "Unless you are circumcised as required by the law of Moses, you cannot be saved." 2 Paul and Barnabas disagreed with them, arguing vehemently. Finally, the church decided to send Paul and Barnabas to Jerusalem, accompanied by some local believers, to talk to the apostles and elders about this question. 3 The church sent the delegates to Jerusalem, and they stopped along the way in Phoenicia and Samaria to visit the believers. They told them—much to everyone's joy—that the Gentiles, too, were being converted.

4 When they arrived in Jerusalem, Barnabas and Paul were welcomed by the whole church, including the apostles and elders. They reported everything God had done through them. 5 But then some of the believers who belonged to the sect of the Pharisees stood up and insisted, "The Gentile converts must be circumcised and required to follow the law of Moses."

6 So the apostles and elders met together to resolve this issue. 7 At the meeting, after a long discussion, Peter stood and addressed them as follows: "Brothers, you all know that God chose me from among you some time ago to preach to the Gentiles so that they could hear the Good News and believe. 8 God knows people's hearts, and he confirmed that he accepts Gentiles by giving them the Holy Spirit, just as he did to us. 9 He made no distinction between us and them, for he cleansed their hearts through faith.

10 So why are you now challenging God by burdening the Gentile believers with a yoke that neither we nor our ancestors were able to bear? 11 We believe that we are all saved the same way, by the undeserved grace of the Lord Jesus."

12 Everyone listened quietly as Barnabas and Paul told about the miraculous signs and wonders God had done through them among the Gentiles.

13 When they had finished, James stood and said, "Brothers, listen to me. 14 Peter has told you about the time God first visited the Gentiles to take from them a people for himself.

15 And this conversion of Gentiles is exactly what the prophets predicted. As it is written:

16 'Afterward I will return
  and restore the fallen house of David.
I will rebuild its ruins
  and restore it,

17 so that the rest of humanity might seek the Lord, including the Gentiles—
  all those I have called to be mine.
The Lord has spoken—

18 he who made these things known so long ago.'

19 "And so my judgment is that we should not make it difficult for the Gentiles who are turning to God. 20 Instead, we should write and tell them to abstain from eating food offered to idols, from sexual immorality, from eating the meat of strangled animals, and from consuming blood. 21 For these laws of Moses have been preached in Jewish synagogues in every city on every Sabbath for many generations."

The Letter for Gentile Believers
Acts 15:22-35

22 Then the apostles and elders together with the whole church in Jerusalem chose delegates, and they sent them to Antioch of Syria with Paul and Barnabas to report on this decision. The men chosen were two of the church leaders—Judas (also called Barsabbas) and Silas. 23 This is the letter they took with them:

"This letter is from the apostles and elders, your brothers in Jerusalem. It is written to the Gentile believers in Antioch, Syria, and Cilicia. Greetings!

24 "We understand that some men from here have troubled you and upset you with their teaching, but we did not send them! 25 So we decided, having come to complete agreement, to send you official representatives, along with our beloved Barnabas and Paul, 26 who have risked their lives for the name of our Lord Jesus Christ. 27 We are sending Judas and Silas to confirm what we have decided concerning your question.

28 "For it seemed good to the Holy Spirit and to us to lay no greater burden on you than these few requirements: 29 You must abstain from eating food offered to idols, from consuming blood or the meat of strangled animals, and from sexual immorality. If you do this, you will do well. Farewell."

30 The messengers went at once to Antioch, where they called a general meeting of the believers and delivered the letter. 31 And there was great joy throughout the church that day as they read this encouraging message.

32 Then Judas and Silas, both being prophets, spoke at length to the believers, encouraging and strengthening their faith. 33 They stayed for a while, and then the believers sent them back to the church in Jerusalem with a blessing of peace. 35 Paul and Barnabas stayed in Antioch. They and many others taught and preached the word of the Lord there.

Reflect.

At the heart of the Council of Jerusalem is a major illustration of the conflict between Christ and conventional culture. It is coming at a time of expansion and multiplication and mishandled it could cause a division within the church.

1. What is the main issue at the heart of the council of Jerusalem?

2. The passage opens by informing us that some of the key players "disagreed vehemently." How do you feel about that? Is it okay to have vehement disagreements within a church?

3. How do you know when the disagreement is for a good cause vs. when it is simply of our own flesh?

4. What are your thoughts about the process of how the council met together and decided the issue?

5. What are your thoughts about how the decision was communicated to the people?

6. What are some principles that can be learned and applied to your life and leadership?

Paul and Barnabas Separate
Acts 15:36-41

36 After some time Paul said to Barnabas, "Let's go back and visit each city where we previously preached the word of the Lord, to see how the new believers are doing." 37 Barnabas agreed and wanted to take along John Mark. 38 But Paul disagreed strongly, since John Mark had deserted them in Pamphylia and had not continued with them in their work. 39 Their disagreement was so sharp that they separated. Barnabas took John Mark with him and sailed for Cyprus. 40 Paul chose Silas, and as he left, the believers entrusted him to the Lord's gracious care. 41 Then he traveled throughout Syria and Cilicia, strengthening the churches there.

Respond.

Reflect.

Just prior to the second missionary journey and immediately following a major victory over the possibility of division at the council of Jerusalem is a disagreement between Paul and Barnabas over John Mark.

First, consider the disagreement and reflect on how each member of the team would have felt.

a. Who would be the person you would naturally have been inclined to side with in this particular situation?

b. Why?

Second, compare and contrast this conflict with the one solved in the council of Jerusalem.

a. What makes these conflicts similar?

b. What makes them different?

Both conflicts are potential opportunities for the enemy of God's mission to thwart the spread of the gospel through division.

a. Do you think one is more or less important than the other?

b. Do you think one could have been avoided in a different way?

c. What are the principles that can be learned and applied from this second conflict?

Paul's Second Missionary Journey
Acts 16-18

The Second Missionary Journey of Paul

Study the second missionary journey of Paul and prepare a formal presentation.

Where did he go? What happened? What patterns emerge from the process of what happened? Patterns of persecution; patterns of the Spirit of God at work; patterns of salvation. What principles can be applied? How would you teach this to someone else?

Your assignment is to make a presentation of the second missionary journey of Paul that demonstrates personal understanding and teaches the content in a meaningful and engaging way. You can be creative and use media or any form of audio/visual communication. You can also work in team, but each member of your team must demonstrate full participation in the final presentation and must turn-in notes from their study of the passage.

For each member of your team, you are allowed one minute of content presentation. Be wise in the number of people who are in your group. If you choose too large a group, then it may be difficult to keep everyone involved, and your presentation may run so long that it is less than engaging. If you choose too small of a group, then you will have difficulty presenting all of the various parts of the content in the amount of time.

Hint: Have your entire group study the whole passage individually first and then assign different sections to different people for the actual presentation. Then work together to find the common themes and common patterns that outline the entire journey. Finally put together a cohesive script. Film each part of the presentation and then edit it together into one larger presentation that meets the time constraints.

Note that because there are so many different locations that are a part of this second journey that you will want to consider editing the video in a manner that recognizes natural thematic breaks and location shifts throughout the journey. For this second presentation your team will also need to create a "study guide" or bible study to accompany your video presentation.

Acts 16:1-5

Paul went first to Derbe and then to Lystra, where there was a young disciple named Timothy. His mother was a Jewish believer, but his father was a Greek. 2 Timothy was well thought of by the believers in Lystra and Iconium, 3 so Paul wanted him to join them on their journey. In deference to the Jews of the area, he arranged for Timothy to be circumcised before they left, for everyone knew that his father was a Greek. 4 Then they went from town to town,
instructing the believers to follow the decisions made by the apostles and elders in Jerusalem. 5 So the churches were strengthened in their faith and grew larger every day.

Acts 16:6-10

6 Next Paul and Silas traveled through the area of Phrygia and Galatia, because the Holy Spirit had prevented them from preaching the word in the province of Asia at that time. 7 Then coming to the borders of Mysia, they headed north for the province of Bithynia, but again the Spirit of Jesus did not allow them to go there. 8 So instead, they went on through Mysia to the seaport of Troas.

9 That night Paul had a vision: A man from Macedonia in northern Greece was standing there, pleading with him, "Come over to Macedonia and help us!" 10 So we decided to leave for Macedonia at once, having concluded that God was calling us to preach the Good News there.

Lydia of Philippi Believes in Jesus (the journey continues)
Acts 16:11-15

11 We boarded a boat at Troas and sailed straight across to the island of Samothrace, and the next day we landed at Neapolis. 12 From there we reached Philippi, a major city of that district of Macedonia and a Roman colony. And we stayed there several days.
13 On the Sabbath we went a little way outside the city to a riverbank, where we thought people would be meeting for prayer, and we sat down to speak with some women who had gathered there. 14 One of them was Lydia from Thyatira, a merchant of expensive purple cloth, who worshiped God. As she listened to us, the Lord opened her heart, and she accepted what Paul was saying. 15 She and her household were baptized, and she asked us to be her guests. "If you agree that I am a true believer in the Lord," she said, "come and stay at my home." And she urged us until we agreed.

16 One day as we were going down to the place of prayer, we met a slave girl who had a spirit that enabled her to tell the future. She earned a lot of money for her masters by telling fortunes. 17 She followed Paul and the rest of us, shouting, "These men are servants of the Most High God, and they have come to tell you how to be saved."
18 This went on day after day until Paul got so exasperated that he turned and said to the demon within her, "I command you in the name of Jesus Christ to come out of her." And instantly it left her.
19 Her masters' hopes of wealth were now shattered, so they grabbed Paul and Silas and dragged them before the authorities at the marketplace. 20 "The whole city is in an uproar because of these Jews!" they shouted to the city officials. 21 "They are teaching customs that are illegal for us Romans to practice."

22 A mob quickly formed against Paul and Silas, and the city officials ordered them stripped and beaten with wooden rods. 23 They were severely beaten, and then they were thrown into prison. The jailer was ordered to make sure they didn't escape.

24 So the jailer put them into the inner dungeon and clamped their feet in the stocks.
25 Around midnight Paul and Silas were praying and singing hymns to God, and the other prisoners were listening. 26 Suddenly, there was a massive earthquake, and the prison was shaken to its foundations. All the doors immediately flew open, and the chains of every prisoner fell off! 27 The jailer woke up to see the prison doors wide open. He assumed the prisoners had escaped, so he drew his sword to kill himself. 28 But Paul shouted to him, "Stop! Don't kill yourself! We are all here!"
29 The jailer called for lights and ran to the dungeon and fell down trembling before Paul and Silas. 30 Then he brought them out and asked, "Sirs, what must I do to be saved?"

31 They replied, "Believe in the Lord Jesus and you will be saved, along with everyone in your household." 32 And they shared the word of the Lord with him and with all who lived in his household. 33 Even at that hour of the night, the jailer cared for them and washed their wounds. Then he and everyone in his household were immediately baptized. 34 He brought them into his house and set a meal before them, and he and his entire household rejoiced because they all believed in God.
35 The next morning the city officials sent the police to tell the jailer, "Let those men go!"
36 So the jailer told Paul, "The city officials have said you and Silas are free to leave. Go in peace."
37 But Paul replied, "They have publicly beaten us without a trial and put us in prison—and we are Roman citizens. So now they want us to leave secretly? Certainly not! Let them come themselves to release us!"
38 When the police reported this, the city officials were alarmed to learn that Paul and Silas were Roman citizens. 39 So they came to the jail and apologized to them. Then they brought them out and begged them to leave the city. 40 When Paul and Silas left the prison, they returned to the home of Lydia. There they met with the believers and encouraged them once more. Then they left town.

Paul and Silas in Prison (the journey continues)
Acts 16:16-40

Once when we were going to the place of prayer, we were met by a female slave who had a spirit by which she predicted the future. She earned a great deal of money for her owners by fortune-telling. 17 She followed Paul and the rest of us, shouting, "These men are servants of the Most High God, who are telling you the way to be saved." 18 She kept this up for many days. Finally Paul became so annoyed that he turned around and said to the spirit, "In the name of Jesus Christ I command you to come out of her!" At that moment the spirit left her.

19 When her owners realized that their hope of making money was gone, they seized Paul and Silas and dragged them into the marketplace to face the authorities. 20 They brought them before the magistrates and said, "These men are Jews, and are throwing our city into an uproar 21 by advocating customs unlawful for us Romans to accept or practice."

22 The crowd joined in the attack against Paul and Silas, and the magistrates ordered them to be stripped and beaten with rods. 23 After they had been severely flogged, they were thrown into prison, and the jailer was commanded to guard them carefully. 24 When he received these orders, he put them in the inner cell and fastened their feet in the stocks.

25 About midnight Paul and Silas were praying and singing hymns to God, and the other prisoners were listening to them. 26 Suddenly there was such a violent earthquake that the foundations of the prison were shaken. At once all the prison doors flew open, and everyone's chains came loose. 27 The jailer woke up, and when he saw the prison doors open, he drew his sword and was about to kill himself because he thought the prisoners had escaped. 28 But Paul shouted, "Don't harm yourself! We are all here!"

29 The jailer called for lights, rushed in and fell trembling before Paul and Silas. 30 He then brought them out and asked, "Sirs, what must I do to be saved?"

31 They replied, "Believe in the Lord Jesus, and you will be saved—you and your household." 32 Then they spoke the word of the Lord to him and to all the others in his house. 33 At that hour of the night the jailer took them and washed their wounds; then immediately he and all his household were baptized. 34 The jailer brought them into his house and set a meal before them; he was filled with joy because he had come to believe in God—he and his whole household.

35 When it was daylight, the magistrates sent their officers to the jailer with the order: "Release those men." 36 The jailer told Paul, "The magistrates have ordered that you and Silas be released. Now you can leave. Go in peace."

37 But Paul said to the officers: "They beat us publicly without a trial, even though we are Roman citizens, and threw us into prison. And now do they want to get rid of us quietly? No! Let them come themselves and escort us out."

38 The officers reported this to the magistrates, and when they heard that Paul and Silas were Roman citizens, they were alarmed. 39 They came to appease them and escorted them from the prison, requesting them to leave the city. 40 After Paul and Silas came out of the prison, they went to Lydia's house, where they met with the brothers and sisters and encouraged them. Then they left.

Paul Preaches in Thessalonica and Berea (the journey continues)
Acts 17:1-15

Paul and Silas then traveled through the towns of Amphipolis and Apollonia and came to Thessalonica, where there was a Jewish synagogue. 2 As was Paul's custom, he went to the synagogue service, and for three Sabbaths in a row he used the Scriptures to reason with the people. 3 He explained the prophecies and proved that the Messiah must suffer and rise from the dead. He said, "This Jesus I'm telling you about is the Messiah." 4 Some of the Jews who listened were persuaded and joined Paul and Silas, along with many God-fearing Greek men and quite a few prominent women.

5 But some of the Jews were jealous, so they gathered some troublemakers from the marketplace to form a mob and start a riot. They attacked the home of Jason, searching for Paul and Silas so they could drag them out to the crowd. 6 Not finding them there, they dragged out Jason and some of the other believers instead and took them before the city council. "Paul and Silas have caused trouble all over the world," they shouted, "and now they are here disturbing our city, too. 7 And Jason has welcomed them into his home. They are all guilty of treason against Caesar, for they profess allegiance to another king, named Jesus."
8 The people of the city, as well as the city council, were thrown into turmoil by these reports. 9 So the officials forced Jason and the other believers to post bond, and then they released them.

10 That very night the believers sent Paul and Silas to Berea. When they arrived there, they went to the Jewish synagogue. 11 And the people of Berea were more open-minded than those in Thessalonica, and they listened eagerly to Paul's message. They searched the Scriptures day after day to see if Paul and Silas were teaching the truth. 12 As a result, many Jews believed, as did many of the prominent Greek women and men.

13 But when some Jews in Thessalonica learned that Paul was preaching the word of God in Berea, they went there and stirred up trouble. 14 The believers acted at once, sending Paul on to the coast, while Silas and Timothy remained behind. 15 Those escorting Paul went with him all the way to Athens; then they returned to Berea with instructions for Silas and Timothy to hurry and join him.

Respond.

Reflect.

Paul Preaches in Athens (the journey continues)
Acts 17:24-34

16 While Paul was waiting for them in Athens, he was deeply troubled by all the idols he saw everywhere in the city. 17 He went to the synagogue to reason with the Jews and the God-fearing Gentiles, and he spoke daily in the public square to all who happened to be there.

18 He also had a debate with some of the Epicurean and Stoic philosophers. When he told them about Jesus and his resurrection, they said, "What's this babbler trying to say with these strange ideas he's picked up?" Others said, "He seems to be preaching about some foreign gods."

19 Then they took him to the high council of the city. "Come and tell us about this new teaching," they said. 20 "You are saying some rather strange things, and we want to know what it's all about." 21 (It should be explained that all the Athenians as well as the foreigners in Athens seemed to spend all their time discussing the latest ideas.)

22 So Paul, standing before the council, addressed them as follows: "Men of Athens, I notice that you are very religious in every way, 23 for as I was walking along I saw your many shrines. And one of your altars had this inscription on it: 'To an Unknown God.' This God, whom you worship without knowing, is the one I'm telling you about.

24 "He is the God who made the world and everything in it. Since he is Lord of heaven and earth, he doesn't live in man-made temples, 25 and human hands can't serve his needs—for he has no needs. He himself gives life and breath to everything, and he satisfies every need.

26 From one man he created all the nations throughout the whole earth. He decided beforehand when they should rise and fall, and he determined their boundaries.

27 "His purpose was for the nations to seek after God and perhaps feel their way toward him and find him—though he is not far from any one of us. 28 For in him we live and move and exist. As some of your own poets have said, 'We are his offspring.' 29 And since this is true, we shouldn't think of God as an idol designed by craftsmen from gold or silver or stone.

30 "God overlooked people's ignorance about these things in earlier times, but now he commands everyone everywhere to repent of their sins and turn to him. 31 For he has set a day for judging the world with justice by the man he has appointed, and he proved to everyone who this is by raising him from the dead."

32 When they heard Paul speak about the resurrection of the dead, some laughed in contempt, but others said, "We want to hear more about this later." 33 That ended Paul's discussion with them, 34 but some joined him and became believers. Among them were Dionysius, a member of the council, a woman named Damaris, and others with them.

Respond.

Paul Meets Priscilla and Aquila in Corinth (the journey continues)
Acts 18:1-17

Then Paul left Athens and went to Corinth. 2 There he became acquainted with a Jew named Aquila, born in Pontus, who had recently arrived from Italy with his wife, Priscilla. They had left Italy when Claudius Caesar deported all Jews from Rome. 3 Paul lived and worked with them, for they were tentmakers just as he was.

4 Each Sabbath found Paul at the synagogue, trying to convince the Jews and Greeks alike. 5 And after Silas and Timothy came down from Macedonia, Paul spent all his time preaching the word. He testified to the Jews that Jesus was the Messiah. 6 But when they opposed and insulted him, Paul shook the dust from his clothes and said, "Your blood is upon your own heads—I am innocent. From now on I will go preach to the Gentiles."

7 Then he left and went to the home of Titius Justus, a Gentile who worshiped God and lived next door to the synagogue. 8 Crispus, the leader of the synagogue, and everyone in his household believed in the Lord. Many others in Corinth also heard Paul, became believers, and were baptized.

9 One night the Lord spoke to Paul in a vision and told him, "Don't be afraid! Speak out! Don't be silent! 10 For I am with you, and no one will attack and harm you, for many people in this city belong to me." 11 So Paul stayed there for the next year and a half, teaching the word of God.

12 But when Gallio became governor of Achaia, some Jews rose up together against Paul and brought him before the governor for judgment. 13 They accused Paul of "persuading people to worship God in ways that are contrary to our law."

14 But just as Paul started to make his defense, Gallio turned to Paul's accusers and said, "Listen, you Jews, if this were a case involving some wrongdoing or a serious crime, I would have a reason to accept your case.

15 But since it is merely a question of words and names and your Jewish law, take care of it yourselves. I refuse to judge such matters." 16 And he threw them out of the courtroom.

17 The crowd then grabbed Sosthenes, the leader of the synagogue, and beat him right there in the courtroom. But Gallio paid no attention.

Respond.

Reflect.

Paul Returns to Antioch of Syria (the journey continues)
Acts 18:18-28

18 Paul stayed in Corinth for some time after that, then said good-bye to the brothers and sisters and went to nearby Cenchrea. There he shaved his head according to Jewish custom, marking the end of a vow. Then he set sail for Syria, taking Priscilla and Aquila with him.

19 They stopped first at the port of Ephesus, where Paul left the others behind. While he was there, he went to the synagogue to reason with the Jews. 20 They asked him to stay longer, but he declined. 21 As he left, however, he said, "I will come back later, God willing." Then he set sail from Ephesus. 22 The next stop was at the port of Caesarea. From there he went up and visited the church at Jerusalem and then went back to Antioch.

23 After spending some time in Antioch, Paul went back through Galatia and Phrygia, visiting and strengthening all the believers.

24 Meanwhile, a Jew named Apollos, an eloquent speaker who knew the Scriptures well, had arrived in Ephesus from Alexandria in Egypt. 25 He had been taught the way of the Lord, and he taught others about Jesus with an enthusiastic spirit and with accuracy. However, he knew only about John's baptism. 26 When Priscilla and Aquila heard him preaching boldly in the synagogue, they took him aside and explained the way of God even more accurately.

27 Apollos had been thinking about going to Achaia, and the brothers and sisters in Ephesus encouraged him to go. They wrote to the believers in Achaia, asking them to welcome him. When he arrived there, he proved to be of great benefit to those who, by God's grace, had believed. 28 He refuted the Jews with powerful arguments in public debate. Using the Scriptures, he explained to them that Jesus was the Messiah.

Respond.

Reflect.

Paul's Third Missionary Journey
Acts 19

The Third Missionary Journey of Paul

Study the third missionary journey of Paul and prepare a formal presentation.

Where did he go? What happened? What patterns emerge from the process of what happened? Patterns of persecution; patterns of the Spirit of God at work; patterns of salvation. What principles can be applied? How would you teach this to someone else?

Your assignment is to make a presentation of the third missionary journey of Paul that demonstrates personal understanding and teaches the content in a meaningful and engaging way. You can be creative and use media or any form of audio/visual communication. You can also work in a team, but each member of your team must demonstrate full participation in the final presentation and must turn-in notes from their study of the passage.

For each member of your team, you are allowed one minute of content presentation. Be wise in the number of people who are in your group. If you choose too large a group, then it may be difficult to keep everyone involved, and your presentation may run so long that it is less than engaging. If you choose too small of a group, then you will have difficulty presenting all of the various parts of the content in the amount of time.

Hint: Have your entire group study the whole passage individually first and then assign different sections to different people for the actual presentation. Then work together to find the common themes and common patterns that outline the entire journey. Finally put together a cohesive script. Film each part of the presentation and then edit it together into one larger presentation that meets the time constraints.

Note that because there are so many different locations that are a part of this third journey that you will want to consider editing the video in a manner that recognizes natural thematic breaks and location shifts throughout the journey. For this third presentation your team will need to create a "study guide" or bible study to accompany your video presentation.

Acts 19:1-6

While Apollos was in Corinth, Paul traveled through the interior regions until he reached Ephesus, on the coast, where he found several believers. 2 "Did you receive the Holy Spirit when you believed?" he asked them.
"No," they replied, "we haven't even heard that there is a Holy Spirit."
3 "Then what baptism did you experience?" he asked. And they replied, "The baptism of John."

4 Paul said, "John's baptism called for repentance from sin. But John himself told the people to believe in the one who would come later, meaning Jesus."
5 As soon as they heard this, they were baptized in the name of the Lord Jesus. 6 Then when Paul laid his hands on them, the Holy Spirit came on them, and they spoke in other tongues and prophesied. 7 There were about twelve men in all.

Paul Ministers in Ephesus (the journey continues)
Acts 19:8-22

8 Then Paul went to the synagogue and preached boldly for the next three months, arguing persuasively about the Kingdom of God. 9 But some became stubborn, rejecting his message and publicly speaking against the Way. So Paul left the synagogue and took the believers with him. Then he held daily discussions at the lecture hall of Tyrannus. 10 This went on for the next two years, so that people throughout the province of Asia–both Jews and Greeks–heard the word of the Lord.
11 God gave Paul the power to perform unusual miracles. 12 When handkerchiefs or aprons that had merely touched his skin were placed on sick people, they were healed of their diseases, and evil spirits were expelled.
13 A group of Jews was traveling from town to town casting out evil spirits. They tried to use the name of the Lord Jesus in their incantation, saying, "I command you in the name of Jesus, whom Paul preaches, to come out!" 14 Seven sons of Sceva, a leading priest, were doing this. 15 But one time when they tried it, the evil spirit replied, "I know Jesus, and I know Paul, but who are you?"

16 Then the man with the evil spirit leaped on them, overpowered them, and attacked them with such violence that they fled from the house, naked and battered.
17 The story of what happened spread quickly all through Ephesus, to Jews and Greeks alike. A solemn fear descended on the city, and the name of the Lord Jesus was greatly honored. 18 Many who became believers confessed their sinful practices. 19 A number of them who had been practicing sorcery brought their incantation books and burned them at a public bonfire. The value of the books was several million dollars. 20 So the message about the Lord spread widely and had a powerful effect.
21 Afterward Paul felt compelled by the Spirit to go over to Macedonia and Achaia before going to Jerusalem. "And after that," he said, "I must go on to Rome!" 22 He sent his two assistants, Timothy and Erastus, ahead to Macedonia while he stayed awhile longer in the province of Asia.

Respond.

Reflect.

The Riot in Ephesus (the journey continues)
Acts 19:23-41

23 About that time, serious trouble developed in Ephesus concerning the Way. 24 It began with Demetrius, a silversmith who had a large business manufacturing silver shrines of the Greek goddess Artemis. He kept many craftsmen busy. 25 He called them together, along with others employed in similar trades, and addressed them as follows:

"Gentlemen, you know that our wealth comes from this business. 26 But as you have seen and heard, this man Paul has persuaded many people that handmade gods aren't really gods at all. And he's done this not only here in Ephesus but throughout the entire province! 27 Of course, I'm not just talking about the loss of public respect for our business. I'm also concerned that the temple of the great goddess Artemis will lose its influence and that Artemis—this magnificent goddess worshiped throughout the province of Asia and all around the world—will be robbed of her great prestige!"

28 At this their anger boiled, and they began shouting, "Great is Artemis of the Ephesians!" 29 Soon the whole city was filled with confusion. Everyone rushed to the amphitheater, dragging along Gaius and Aristarchus, who were Paul's traveling companions from Macedonia. 30 Paul wanted to go in, too, but the believers wouldn't let him. 31 Some of the officials of the province, friends of Paul, also sent a message to him, begging him not to risk his life by entering the amphitheater.

32 Inside, the people were all shouting, some one thing and some another. Everything was in confusion. In fact, most of them didn't even know why they were there. 33 The Jews in the crowd pushed Alexander forward and told him to explain the situation. He motioned for silence and tried to speak. 34 But when the crowd realized he was a Jew, they started shouting again and kept it up for about two hours: "Great is Artemis of the Ephesians! Great is Artemis of the Ephesians!"

35 At last the mayor was able to quiet them down enough to speak. "Citizens of Ephesus," he said. "Everyone knows that Ephesus is the official guardian of the temple of the great Artemis, whose image fell down to us from heaven. 36 Since this is an undeniable fact, you should stay calm and not do anything rash. 37 You have brought these men here, but they have stolen nothing from the temple and have not spoken against our goddess.

38 "If Demetrius and the craftsmen have a case against them, the courts are in session and the officials can hear the case at once. Let them make formal charges. 39 And if there are complaints about other matters, they can be settled in a legal assembly. 40 I am afraid we are in danger of being charged with rioting by the Roman government, since there is no cause for all this commotion. And if Rome demands an explanation, we won't know what to say." 41 Then he dismissed them, and they dispersed.

Respond.

Reflect.

Paul Goes to Macedonia, Greece and Troas (the journey continues)
Acts 20:1-12

When the uproar was over, Paul sent for the believers and encouraged them. Then he said good-bye and left for Macedonia. 2 While there, he encouraged the believers in all the towns he passed through. Then he traveled down to Greece, 3 where he stayed for three months. He was preparing to sail back to Syria when he discovered a plot by some Jews against his life, so he decided to return through Macedonia.
4 Several men were traveling with him. They were Sopater son of Pyrrhus from Berea; Aristarchus and Secundus from Thessalonica; Gaius from Derbe; Timothy; and Tychicus and Trophimus from the province of Asia. 5 They went on ahead and waited for us at Troas. 6 After the Passover ended, we boarded a ship at Philippi in Macedonia and five days later joined them in Troas, where we stayed a week.

7 On the first day of the week, we gathered with the local believers to share in the Lord's Supper. Paul was preaching to them, and since he was leaving the next day, he kept talking until midnight. 8 The upstairs room where we met was lighted with many flickering lamps. 9 As Paul spoke on and on, a young man named Eutychus, sitting on the windowsill, became very drowsy. Finally, he fell sound asleep and dropped three stories to his death below. 10 Paul went down, bent over him, and took him into his arms. "Don't worry," he said, "he's alive!" 11 Then they all went back upstairs, shared in the Lord's Supper, and ate together. Paul continued talking to them until dawn, and then he left. 12 Meanwhile, the young man was taken home alive and well, and everyone was greatly relieved.

Respond.

Reflect.

Paul Meets the Ephesian Elders (the journey continues)
Acts 20:13-38

13 Paul went by land to Assos, where he had arranged for us to join him, while we traveled by ship. 14 He joined us there, and we sailed together to Mitylene. 15 The next day we sailed past the island of Kios. The following day we crossed to the island of Samos, and a day later we arrived at Miletus.

16 Paul had decided to sail on past Ephesus, for he didn't want to spend any more time in the province of Asia. He was hurrying to get to Jerusalem, if possible, in time for the Festival of Pentecost. 17 But when we landed at Miletus, he sent a message to the elders of the church at Ephesus, asking them to come and meet him.

18 When they arrived he declared, "You know that from the day I set foot in the province of Asia until now 19 I have done the Lord's work humbly and with many tears. I have endured the trials that came to me from the plots of the Jews. 20 I never shrank back from telling you what you needed to hear, either publicly or in your homes. 21 I have had one message for Jews and Greeks alike—the necessity of repenting from sin and turning to God, and of having faith in our Lord Jesus.

22 "And now I am bound by the Spirit to go to Jerusalem. I don't know what awaits me, 23 except that the Holy Spirit tells me in city after city that jail and suffering lie ahead. 24 But my life is worth nothing to me unless I use it for finishing the work assigned me by the Lord Jesus—the work of telling others the Good News about the wonderful grace of God.
25 "And now I know that none of you to whom I have preached the Kingdom will ever see me again. 26 I declare today that I have been faithful. If anyone suffers eternal death, it's not my fault, 27 for I didn't shrink from declaring all that God wants you to know.

28 "So guard yourselves and God's people. Feed and shepherd God's flock—his church, purchased with his own blood—over which the Holy Spirit has appointed you as leaders. 29 I know that false teachers, like vicious wolves, will come in among you after I leave, not sparing the flock. 30 Even some men from your own group will rise up and distort the truth in order to draw a following. 31 Watch out! Remember the three years I was with you—my constant watch and care over you night and day, and my many tears for you.

32 "And now I entrust you to God and the message of his grace that is able to build you up and give you an inheritance with all those he has set apart for himself.

33 "I have never coveted anyone's silver or gold or fine clothes. 34 You know that these hands of mine have worked to supply my own needs and even the needs of those who were with me. 35 And I have been a constant example of how you can help those in need by working hard. You should remember the words of the Lord Jesus: 'It is more blessed to give than to receive.'"

36 When he had finished speaking, he knelt and prayed with them. 37 They all cried as they embraced and kissed him good-bye. 38 They were sad most of all because he had said that they would never see him again. Then they escorted him down to the ship.

Paul Returns to Jerusalem (the journey concludes)
Acts 21:1-25

After saying farewell to the Ephesian elders, we sailed straight to the island of Cos. The next day we reached Rhodes and then went to Patara. 2 There we boarded a ship sailing for Phoenicia. 3 We sighted the island of Cyprus, passed it on our left, and landed at the harbor of Tyre, in Syria, where the ship was to unload its cargo.

4 We went ashore, found the local believers,[ed] and stayed with them a week. These believers prophesied through the Holy Spirit that Paul should not go on to Jerusalem. 5 When we returned to the ship at the end of the week, the entire congregation, including women[ee] and children, left the city and came down to the shore with us. There we knelt, prayed, 6 and said our farewells. Then we went aboard, and they returned home.

7 The next stop after leaving Tyre was Ptolemais, where we greeted the brothers and sisters and stayed for one day. 8 The next day we went on to Caesarea and stayed at the home of Philip the Evangelist, one of the seven men who had been chosen to distribute food. 9 He had four unmarried daughters who had the gift of prophecy.

10 Several days later a man named Agabus, who also had the gift of prophecy, arrived from Judea. 11 He came over, took Paul's belt, and bound his own feet and hands with it. Then he said, "The Holy Spirit declares, 'So shall the owner of this belt be bound by the Jewish leaders in Jerusalem and turned over to the Gentiles.'" 12 When we heard this, we and the local believers all begged Paul not to go on to Jerusalem.
13 But he said, "Why all this weeping? You are breaking my heart! I am ready not only to be jailed at Jerusalem but even to die for the sake of the Lord Jesus."

14 When it was clear that we couldn't persuade him, we gave up and said, "The Lord's will be done."

15 After this we packed our things and left for Jerusalem. 16 Some believers from Caesarea accompanied us, and they took us to the home of Mnason, a man originally from Cyprus and one of the early believers. 17 When we arrived, the brothers and sisters in Jerusalem welcomed us warmly.

18 The next day Paul went with us to meet with James, and all the elders of the Jerusalem church were present. 19 After greeting them, Paul gave a detailed account of the things God had accomplished among the Gentiles through his ministry.

20 After hearing this, they praised God. And then they said, "You know, dear brother, how many thousands of Jews have also believed, and they all follow the law of Moses very seriously. 21 But the Jewish believers here in Jerusalem have been told that you are teaching all the Jews who live among the Gentiles to turn their backs on the laws of Moses. They've heard that you teach them not to circumcise their children or follow other Jewish customs. 22 What should we do? They will certainly hear that you have come.

23 "Here's what we want you to do. We have four men here who have completed their vow. 24 Go with them to the Temple and join them in the purification ceremony, paying for them to have their heads ritually shaved. Then everyone will know that the rumors are all false and that you yourself observe the Jewish laws.

25 "As for the Gentile believers, they should do what we already told them in a letter: They should abstain from eating food offered to idols, from consuming blood or the meat of strangled animals, and from sexual immorality."

Paul is Arrested and Speaking to the Crowd
Acts 21:26-40

26 So Paul went to the Temple the next day with the other men. They had already started the purification ritual, so he publicly announced the date when their vows would end and sacrifices would be offered for each of them.

27 The seven days were almost ended when some Jews from the province of Asia saw Paul in the Temple and roused a mob against him. They grabbed him, 28 yelling, "Men of Israel, help us! This is the man who preaches against our people everywhere and tells everybody to disobey the Jewish laws. He speaks against the Temple–and even defiles this holy place by bringing in Gentiles." 29 (For earlier that day they had seen him in the city with Trophimus, a Gentile from Ephesus, and they assumed Paul had taken him into the Temple.)

30 The whole city was rocked by these accusations, and a great riot followed. Paul was grabbed and dragged out of the Temple, and immediately the gates were closed behind him. 31 As they were trying to kill him, word reached the commander of the Roman regiment that all Jerusalem was in an uproar. 32 He immediately called out his soldiers and officers and ran down among the crowd. When the mob saw the commander and the troops coming, they stopped beating Paul.

33 Then the commander arrested him and ordered him bound with two chains. He asked the crowd who he was and what he had done. 34 Some shouted one thing and some another. Since he couldn't find out the truth in all the uproar and confusion, he ordered that Paul be taken to the fortress. 35 As Paul reached the stairs, the mob grew so violent the soldiers had to lift him to their shoulders to protect him. 36 And the crowd followed behind, shouting, "Kill him, kill him!"

37 As Paul was about to be taken inside, he said to the commander, "May I have a word with you?"
"Do you know Greek?" the commander asked, surprised. 38 "Aren't you the Egyptian who led a rebellion some time ago and took 4,000 members of the Assassins out into the desert?"

39 "No," Paul replied, "I am a Jew and a citizen of Tarsus in Cilicia, which is an important city. Please, let me talk to these people." 40 The commander agreed, so Paul stood on the stairs and motioned to the people to be quiet. Soon a deep silence enveloped the crowd, and he addressed them in their own language, Aramaic.

Respond.

Reflect.

The Sermon in Jerusalem
Acts 22:1-23

"Brothers and esteemed fathers," Paul said, "listen to me as I offer my defense." 2 When they heard him speaking in their own language, the silence was even greater.

3 Then Paul said, "I am a Jew, born in Tarsus, a city in Cilicia, and I was brought up and educated here in Jerusalem under Gamaliel. As his student, I was carefully trained in our Jewish laws and customs. I became very zealous to honor God in everything I did, just like all of you today. 4 And I persecuted the followers of the Way, hounding some to death, arresting both men and women and throwing them in prison. 5 The high priest and the whole council of elders can testify that this is so. For I received letters from them to our Jewish brothers in Damascus, authorizing me to bring the followers of the Way from there to Jerusalem, in chains, to be punished.
6 "As I was on the road, approaching Damascus about noon, a very bright light from heaven suddenly shone down around me. 7 I fell to the ground and heard a voice saying to me, 'Saul, Saul, why are you persecuting me?'

8 "'Who are you, lord?' I asked.

"And the voice replied, 'I am Jesus the Nazarene, the one you are persecuting.' 9 The people with me saw the light but didn't understand the voice speaking to me.

10 "I asked, 'What should I do, Lord?'
"And the Lord told me, 'Get up and go into Damascus, and there you will be told everything you are to do.'

11 "I was blinded by the intense light and had to be led by the hand to Damascus by my companions. 12 A man named Ananias lived there. He was a godly man, deeply devoted to the law, and well regarded by all the Jews of Damascus. 13 He came and stood beside me and said, 'Brother Saul, regain your sight.' And that very moment I could see him!

14 "Then he told me, 'The God of our ancestors has chosen you to know his will and to see the Righteous One and hear him speak. 15 For you are to be his witness, telling everyone what you have seen and heard. 16 What are you waiting for? Get up and be baptized. Have your sins washed away by calling on the name of the Lord.'

17 "After I returned to Jerusalem, I was praying in the Temple and fell into a trance. 18 I saw a vision of Jesus saying to me, 'Hurry! Leave Jerusalem, for the people here won't accept your testimony about me.'

19 "'But Lord,' I argued, 'they certainly know that in every synagogue I imprisoned and beat those who believed in you. 20 And I was in complete agreement when your witness Stephen was killed. I stood by and kept the coats they took off when they stoned him.'
21 "But the Lord said to me, 'Go, for I will send you far away to the Gentiles!'"

22 The crowd listened until Paul said that word. Then they all began to shout, "Away with such a fellow! He isn't fit to live!" 23 They yelled, threw off their coats, and tossed handfuls of dust into the air.

Respond.

Reflect.

Paul before the High Council
Acts 22:24 - 23:1-11

24 The commander brought Paul inside and ordered him lashed with whips to make him confess his crime. He wanted to find out why the crowd had become so furious. 25 When they tied Paul down to lash him, Paul said to the officer standing there, "Is it legal for you to whip a Roman citizen who hasn't even been tried?"

26 When the officer heard this, he went to the commander and asked, "What are you doing? This man is a Roman citizen!"

27 So the commander went over and asked Paul, "Tell me, are you a Roman citizen?"

"Yes, I certainly am," Paul replied.

28 "I am, too," the commander muttered, "and it cost me plenty!"

Paul answered, "But I am a citizen by birth!"

29 The soldiers who were about to interrogate Paul quickly withdrew when they heard he was a Roman citizen, and the commander was frightened because he had ordered him bound and whipped.

30 The next day the commander ordered the leading priests into session with the Jewish high council. He wanted to find out what the trouble was all about, so he released Paul to have him stand before them.

Gazing intently at the high council, Paul began: "Brothers, I have always lived before God with a clear conscience!"

2 Instantly Ananias the high priest commanded those close to Paul to slap him on the mouth. 3 But Paul said to him, "God will slap you, you corrupt hypocrite! What kind of judge are you to break the law yourself by ordering me struck like that?"

4 Those standing near Paul said to him, "Do you dare to insult God's high priest?"

5 "I'm sorry, brothers. I didn't realize he was the high priest," Paul replied, "for the Scriptures say, 'You must not speak evil of any of your rulers.'"

6 Paul realized that some members of the high council were Sadducees and some were Pharisees, so he shouted, "Brothers, I am a Pharisee, as were my ancestors! And I am on trial because my hope is in the resurrection of the dead!"

7 This divided the council—the Pharisees against the Sadducees— 8 for the Sadducees say there is no resurrection or angels or spirits, but the Pharisees believe in all of these. 9 So there was a great uproar. Some of the teachers of religious law who were Pharisees jumped up and began to argue forcefully. "We see nothing wrong with him," they shouted. "Perhaps a spirit or an angel spoke to him."

10 As the conflict grew more violent, the commander was afraid they would tear Paul apart. So he ordered his soldiers to go and rescue him by force and take him back to the fortress.

11 That night the Lord appeared to Paul and said, "Be encouraged, Paul. Just as you have been a witness to me here in Jerusalem, you must preach the Good News in Rome as well."

The Plan to Kill Paul and Paul Sent to Caesarea
Acts 23:12-35

12 The next morning a group of Jews got together and bound themselves with an oath not to eat or drink until they had killed Paul. 13 There were more than forty of them in the conspiracy. 14 They went to the leading priests and elders and told them, "We have bound ourselves with an oath to eat nothing until we have killed Paul. 15 So you and the high council should ask the commander to bring Paul back to the council again. Pretend you want to examine his case more fully. We will kill him on the way."

16 But Paul's nephew—his sister's son—heard of their plan and went to the fortress and told Paul. 17 Paul called for one of the Roman officers and said, "Take this young man to the commander. He has something important to tell him."

18 So the officer did, explaining, "Paul, the prisoner, called me over and asked me to bring this young man to you because he has something to tell you."

19 The commander took his hand, led him aside, and asked, "What is it you want to tell me?"

20 Paul's nephew told him, "Some Jews are going to ask you to bring Paul before the high council tomorrow, pretending they want to get some more information. 21 But don't do it! There are more than forty men hiding along the way ready to ambush him. They have vowed not to eat or drink anything until they have killed him. They are ready now, just waiting for your consent."

22 "Don't let anyone know you told me this," the commander warned the young man.

23 Then the commander called two of his officers and ordered, "Get 200 soldiers ready to leave for Caesarea at nine o'clock tonight. Also take 200 spearmen and 70 mounted troops. 24 Provide horses for Paul to ride, and get him safely to Governor Felix." 25 Then he wrote this letter to the governor:

26 "From Claudius Lysias, to his Excellency, Governor Felix: Greetings!

27 "This man was seized by some Jews, and they were about to kill him when I arrived with the troops. When I learned that he was a Roman citizen, I removed him to safety. 28 Then I took him to their high council to try to learn the basis of the accusations against him. 29 I soon discovered the charge was something regarding their religious law—certainly nothing worthy of imprisonment or death. 30 But when I was informed of a plot to kill him, I immediately sent him on to you. I have told his accusers to bring their charges before you."

31 So that night, as ordered, the soldiers took Paul as far as Antipatris. 32 They returned to the fortress the next morning, while the mounted troops took him on to Caesarea. 33 When they arrived in Caesarea, they presented Paul and the letter to Governor Felix. 34 He read it and then asked Paul what province he was from. "Cilicia," Paul answered. 35 "I will hear your case myself when your accusers arrive," the governor told him. Then the governor ordered him kept in the prison at Herod's headquarters.

Paul Appears before Felix

Acts 24:1-27

Five days later Ananias, the high priest, arrived with some of the Jewish elders and the lawyer Tertullus, to present their case against Paul to the governor. 2 When Paul was called in, Tertullus presented the charges against Paul in the following address to the governor:

"You have provided a long period of peace for us Jews and with foresight have enacted reforms for us. 3 For all of this, Your Excellency, we are very grateful to you. 4 But I don't want to bore you, so please give me your attention for only a moment. 5 We have found this man to be a troublemaker who is constantly stirring up riots among the Jews all over the world. He is a ringleader of the cult known as the Nazarenes. 6 Furthermore, he was trying to desecrate the Temple when we arrested him. 8 You can find out the truth of our accusations by examining him yourself."

9 Then the other Jews chimed in, declaring that everything Tertullus said was true.

10 The governor then motioned for Paul to speak. Paul said, "I know, sir, that you have been a judge of Jewish affairs for many years, so I gladly present my defense before you. 11 You can quickly discover that I arrived in Jerusalem no more than twelve days ago to worship at the Temple. 12 My accusers never found me arguing with anyone in the Temple, nor stirring up a riot in any synagogue or on the streets of the city. 13 These men cannot prove the things they accuse me of doing.

14 "But I admit that I follow the Way, which they call a cult. I worship the God of our ancestors, and I firmly believe the Jewish law and everything written in the prophets. 15 I have the same hope in God that these men have, that he will raise both the righteous and the unrighteous. 16 Because of this, I always try to maintain a clear conscience before God and all people.

17 "After several years away, I returned to Jerusalem with money to aid my people and to offer sacrifices to God. 18 My accusers saw me in the Temple as I was completing a purification ceremony. There was no crowd around me and no rioting. 19 But some Jews from the province of Asia were there—and they ought to be here to bring charges if they have anything against me! 20 Ask these men here what crime the Jewish high council found me guilty of, 21 except for the one time I shouted out, 'I am on trial before you today because I believe in the resurrection of the dead!'"

22 At that point Felix, who was quite familiar with the Way, adjourned the hearing and said, "Wait until Lysias, the garrison commander, arrives. Then I will decide the case." 23 He ordered an officer[ey] to keep Paul in custody but to give him some freedom and allow his friends to visit him and take care of his needs.

24 A few days later Felix came back with his wife, Drusilla, who was Jewish. Sending for Paul, they listened as he told them about faith in Christ Jesus. 25 As he reasoned with them about righteousness and self-control and the coming day of judgment, Felix became frightened. "Go away for now," he replied. "When it is more convenient, I'll call for you again." 26 He also hoped that Paul would bribe him, so he sent for him quite often and talked with him.

27 After two years went by in this way, Felix was succeeded by Porcius Festus. And because Felix wanted to gain favor with the Jewish people, he left Paul in prison.

Paul Appears before Festus
Acts 25:122

Three days after Festus arrived in Caesarea to take over his new responsibilities, he left for Jerusalem, 2 where the leading priests and other Jewish leaders met with him and made their accusations against Paul. 3 They asked Festus as a favor to transfer Paul to Jerusalem (planning to ambush and kill him on the way). 4 But Festus replied that Paul was at Caesarea and he himself would be returning there soon. 5 So he said, "Those of you in authority can return with me. If Paul has done anything wrong, you can make your accusations."

6 About eight or ten days later Festus returned to Caesarea, and on the following day he took his seat in court and ordered that Paul be brought in. 7 When Paul arrived, the Jewish leaders from Jerusalem gathered around and made many serious accusations they couldn't prove.

8 Paul denied the charges. "I am not guilty of any crime against the Jewish laws or the Temple or the Roman government," he said.

9 Then Festus, wanting to please the Jews, asked him, "Are you willing to go to Jerusalem and stand trial before me there?"

10 But Paul replied, "No! This is the official Roman court, so I ought to be tried right here. You know very well I am not guilty of harming the Jews. 11 If I have done something worthy of death, I don't refuse to die. But if I am innocent, no one has a right to turn me over to these men to kill me. I appeal to Caesar!"

12 Festus conferred with his advisers and then replied, "Very well! You have appealed to Caesar, and to Caesar you will go!"

13 A few days later King Agrippa arrived with his sister, Bernice, to pay their respects to Festus. 14 During their stay of several days, Festus discussed Paul's case with the king. "There is a prisoner here," he told him, "whose case was left for me by Felix. 15 When I was in Jerusalem, the leading priests and Jewish elders pressed charges against him and asked me to condemn him. 16 I pointed out to them that Roman law does not convict people without a trial. They must be given an opportunity to confront their accusers and defend themselves.

17 "When his accusers came here for the trial, I didn't delay. I called the case the very next day and ordered Paul brought in. 18 But the accusations made against him weren't any of the crimes I expected. 19 Instead, it was something about their religion and a dead man named Jesus, who Paul insists is alive. 20 I was at a loss to know how to investigate these things, so I asked him whether he would be willing to stand trial on these charges in Jerusalem. 21 But Paul appealed to have his case decided by the emperor. So I ordered that he be held in custody until I could arrange to send him to Caesar."

22 "I'd like to hear the man myself," Agrippa said.

And Festus replied, "You will—tomorrow!"

Paul Speaks to Agrippa
Acts 25:23-27

Respond.

23 So the next day Agrippa and Bernice arrived at the auditorium with great pomp, accompanied by military officers and prominent men of the city. Festus ordered that Paul be brought in. 24 Then Festus said, "King Agrippa and all who are here, this is the man whose death is demanded by all the Jews, both here and in Jerusalem. 25 But in my opinion he has done nothing deserving death. However, since he appealed his case to the emperor, I have decided to send him to Rome. 26 "But what shall I write the emperor? For there is no clear charge against him. So I have brought him before all of you, and especially you, King Agrippa, so that after we examine him, I might have something to write. 27 For it makes no sense to send a prisoner to the emperor without specifying the charges against him!"

Reflect.

Paul before the High Council

Acts 23:1-11

Then Agrippa said to Paul, "You may speak in your defense."

So Paul, gesturing with his hand, started his defense: 2 "I am fortunate, King Agrippa, that you are the one hearing my defense today against all these accusations made by the Jewish leaders, 3 for I know you are an expert on all Jewish customs and controversies. Now please listen to me patiently!

4 "As the Jewish leaders are well aware, I was given a thorough Jewish training from my earliest childhood among my own people and in Jerusalem. 5 If they would admit it, they know that I have been a member of the Pharisees, the strictest sect of our religion. 6 Now I am on trial because of my hope in the fulfillment of God's promise made to our ancestors. 7 In fact, that is why the twelve tribes of Israel zealously worship God night and day, and they share the same hope I have. Yet, Your Majesty, they accuse me for having this hope! 8 Why does it seem incredible to any of you that God can raise the dead?

9 "I used to believe that I ought to do everything I could to oppose the very name of Jesus the Nazarene. 10 Indeed, I did just that in Jerusalem. Authorized by the leading priests, I caused many believers there to be sent to prison. And I cast my vote against them when they were condemned to death. 11 Many times I had them punished in the synagogues to get them to curse Jesus. I was so violently opposed to them that I even chased them down in foreign cities.

12 "One day I was on such a mission to Damascus, armed with the authority and commission of the leading priests. 13 About noon, Your Majesty, as I was on the road, a light from heaven brighter than the sun shone down on me and my companions. 14 We all fell down, and I heard a voice saying to me in Aramaic, 'Saul, Saul, why are you persecuting me? It is useless for you to fight against my will.'

15 "'Who are you, lord?' I asked.

"And the Lord replied, 'I am Jesus, the one you are persecuting. 16 Now get to your feet! For I have appeared to you to appoint you as my servant and witness.

Tell people that you have seen me, and tell them what I will show you in the future.

17 And I will rescue you from both your own people and the Gentiles. Yes, I am sending you to the Gentiles 18 to open their eyes, so they may turn from darkness to light and from the power of Satan to God. Then they will receive forgiveness for their sins and be given a place among God's people, who are set apart by faith in me.'

19 "And so, King Agrippa, I obeyed that vision from heaven. 20 I preached first to those in Damascus, then in Jerusalem and throughout all Judea, and also to the Gentiles, that all must repent of their sins and turn to God—and prove they have changed by the good things they do. 21 Some Jews arrested me in the Temple for preaching this, and they tried to kill me. 22 But God has protected me right up to this present time so I can testify to everyone, from the least to the greatest. I teach nothing except what the prophets and Moses said would happen— 23 that the Messiah would suffer and be the first to rise from the dead, and in this way announce God's light to Jews and Gentiles alike."

24 Suddenly, Festus shouted, "Paul, you are insane. Too much study has made you crazy!"

25 But Paul replied, "I am not insane, Most Excellent Festus. What I am saying is the sober truth. 26 And King Agrippa knows about these things. I speak boldly, for I am sure these events are all familiar to him, for they were not done in a corner! 27 King Agrippa, do you believe the prophets? I know you do—"

28 Agrippa interrupted him. "Do you think you can persuade me to become a Christian so quickly?"

29 Paul replied, "Whether quickly or not, I pray to God that both you and everyone here in this audience might become the same as I am, except for these chains."

30 Then the king, the governor, Bernice, and all the others stood and left. 31 As they went out, they talked it over and agreed, "This man hasn't done anything to deserve death or imprisonment."

32 And Agrippa said to Festus, "He could have been set free if he hadn't appealed to Caesar."

Paul before the High Council
Acts 27:1-12

Respond.

Reflect.

When the time came, we set sail for Italy. Paul and several other prisoners were placed in the custody of a Roman officer named Julius, a captain of the Imperial Regiment. 2 Aristarchus, a Macedonian from Thessalonica, was also with us. We left on a ship whose home port was Adramyttium on the northwest coast of the province of Asia; it was scheduled to make several stops at ports along the coast of the province.

3 The next day when we docked at Sidon, Julius was very kind to Paul and let him go ashore to visit with friends so they could provide for his needs. 4 Putting out to sea from there, we encountered strong headwinds that made it difficult to keep the ship on course, so we sailed north of Cyprus between the island and the mainland. 5 Keeping to the open sea, we passed along the coast of Cilicia and Pamphylia, landing at Myra, in the province of Lycia. 6 There the commanding officer found an Egyptian ship from Alexandria that was bound for Italy, and he put us on board.

7 We had several days of slow sailing, and after great difficulty we finally neared Cnidus. But the wind was against us, so we sailed across to Crete and along the sheltered coast of the island, past the cape of Salmone. 8 We struggled along the coast with great difficulty and finally arrived at Fair Havens, near the town of Lasea. 9 We had lost a lot of time. The weather was becoming dangerous for sea travel because it was so late in the fall,[fi] and Paul spoke to the ship's officers about it.

10 "Men," he said, "I believe there is trouble ahead if we go on—shipwreck, loss of cargo, and danger to our lives as well." 11 But the officer in charge of the prisoners listened more to the ship's captain and the owner than to Paul. 12 And since Fair Havens was an exposed harbor—a poor place to spend the winter—most of the crew wanted to go on to Phoenix, farther up the coast of Crete, and spend the winter there. Phoenix was a good harbor with only a southwest and northwest exposure.

The Storm at Sea
Acts 27:13-26

13 When a light wind began blowing from the south, the sailors thought they could make it. So they pulled up anchor and sailed close to the shore of Crete. 14 But the weather changed abruptly, and a wind of typhoon strength (called a "northeaster") burst across the island and blew us out to sea. 15 The sailors couldn't turn the ship into the wind, so they gave up and let it run before the gale.

16 We sailed along the sheltered side of a small island named Cauda, where with great difficulty we hoisted aboard the lifeboat being towed behind us. 17 Then the sailors bound ropes around the hull of the ship to strengthen it. They were afraid of being driven across to the sandbars of Syrtis off the African coast, so they lowered the sea anchor to slow the ship and were driven before the wind.

18 The next day, as gale-force winds continued to batter the ship, the crew began throwing the cargo overboard. 19 The following day they even took some of the ship's gear and threw it overboard. 20 The terrible storm raged for many days, blotting out the sun and the stars, until at last all hope was gone.

21 No one had eaten for a long time. Finally, Paul called the crew together and said, "Men, you should have listened to me in the first place and not left Crete. You would have avoided all this damage and loss. 22 But take courage! None of you will lose your lives, even though the ship will go down. 23 For last night an angel of the God to whom I belong and whom I serve stood beside me, 24 and he said, 'Don't be afraid, Paul, for you will surely stand trial before Caesar! What's more, God in his goodness has granted safety to everyone sailing with you.' 25 So take courage! For I believe God. It will be just as he said. 26 But we will be shipwrecked on an island."

Respond.

Reflect.

The Shipwreck
Acts 27:27-34

27 About midnight on the fourteenth night of the storm, as we were being driven across the Sea of Adria, the sailors sensed land was near. 28 They dropped a weighted line and found that the water was 120 feet deep. But a little later they measured again and found it was only 90 feet deep. 29 At this rate they were afraid we would soon be driven against the rocks along the shore, so they threw out four anchors from the back of the ship and prayed for daylight.

30 Then the sailors tried to abandon the ship; they lowered the lifeboat as though they were going to put out anchors from the front of the ship. 31 But Paul said to the commanding officer and the soldiers, "You will all die unless the sailors stay aboard." 32 So the soldiers cut the ropes to the lifeboat and let it drift away.

33 Just as day was dawning, Paul urged everyone to eat. "You have been so worried that you haven't touched food for two weeks," he said. 34 "Please eat something now for your own good. For not a hair of your heads will perish." 35 Then he took some bread, gave thanks to God before them all, and broke off a piece and ate it. 36 Then everyone was encouraged and began to eat– 37 all 276 of us who were on board. 38 After eating, the crew lightened the ship further by throwing the cargo of wheat overboard.

39 When morning dawned, they didn't recognize the coastline, but they saw a bay with a beach and wondered if they could get to shore by running the ship aground. 40 So they cut off the anchors and left them in the sea. Then they lowered the rudders, raised the foresail, and headed toward shore. 41 But they hit a shoal and ran the ship aground too soon. The bow of the ship stuck fast, while the stern was repeatedly smashed by the force of the waves and began to break apart.

42 The soldiers wanted to kill the prisoners to make sure they didn't swim ashore and escape. 43 But the commanding officer wanted to spare Paul, so he didn't let them carry out their plan. Then he ordered all who could swim to jump overboard first and make for land. 44 The others held on to planks or debris from the broken ship. So everyone escaped safely to shore.

Respond.

Reflect.

.

.

Paul on the island of Malta
Acts 28:1-10

Once we were safe on shore, we learned that we were on the island of Malta. 2 The people of the island were very kind to us. It was cold and rainy, so they built a fire on the shore to welcome us.

3 As Paul gathered an armful of sticks and was laying them on the fire, a poisonous snake, driven out by the heat, bit him on the hand. 4 The people of the island saw it hanging from his hand and said to each other, "A murderer, no doubt! Though he escaped the sea, justice will not permit him to live." 5 But Paul shook off the snake into the fire and was unharmed. 6 The people waited for him to swell up or suddenly drop dead. But when they had waited a long time and saw that he wasn't harmed, they changed their minds and decided he was a god.

7 Near the shore where we landed was an estate belonging to Publius, the chief official of the island. He welcomed us and treated us kindly for three days. 8 As it happened, Publius's father was ill with fever and dysentery. Paul went in and prayed for him, and laying his hands on him, he healed him. 9 Then all the other sick people on the island came and were healed. 10 As a result we were showered with honors, and when the time came to sail, people supplied us with everything we would need for the trip.

Respond.

Reflect.

Paul Arrives at Rome
Acts 28:11-16

11 It was three months after the shipwreck that we set sail on another ship that had wintered at the island—an Alexandrian ship with the twin gods as its figurehead. 12 Our first stop was Syracuse, where we stayed three days. 13 From there we sailed across to Rhegium. A day later a south wind began blowing, so the following day we sailed up the coast to Puteoli. 14 There we found some believers, who invited us to spend a week with them. And so we came to Rome.

15 The brothers and sisters in Rome had heard we were coming, and they came to meet us at the Forum on the Appian Way. Others joined us at The Three Taverns. When Paul saw them, he was encouraged and thanked God.

16 When we arrived in Rome, Paul was permitted to have his own private lodging, though he was guarded by a soldier.

Respond.

Reflect.

Paul Preaches at Rome under Guard
Acts 28:17-27

17 Three days after Paul's arrival, he called together the local Jewish leaders. He said to them, "Brothers, I was arrested in Jerusalem and handed over to the Roman government, even though I had done nothing against our people or the customs of our ancestors. 18 The Romans tried me and wanted to release me, because they found no cause for the death sentence. 19 But when the Jewish leaders protested the decision, I felt it necessary to appeal to Caesar, even though I had no desire to press charges against my own people. 20 I asked you to come here today so we could get acquainted and so I could explain to you that I am bound with this chain because I believe that the hope of Israel—the Messiah—has already come."
21 They replied, "We have had no letters from Judea or reports against you from anyone who has come here. 22 But we want to hear what you believe, for the only thing we know about this movement is that it is denounced everywhere."

Respond.

23 So a time was set, and on that day a large number of people came to Paul's lodging. He explained and testified about the Kingdom of God and tried to persuade them about Jesus from the Scriptures. Using the law of Moses and the books of the prophets, he spoke to them from morning until evening. 24 Some were persuaded by the things he said, but others did not believe. 25 And after they had argued back and forth among themselves, they left with this final word from Paul: "The Holy Spirit was right when he said to your ancestors through Isaiah the prophet,
26 'Go and say to this people:
When you hear what I say,
    you will not understand.
When you see what I do,
    you will not comprehend.
27 For the hearts of these people are hardened,
    and their ears cannot hear,
    and they have closed their eyes—
so their eyes cannot see,
    and their ears cannot hear,
    and their hearts cannot understand,
and they cannot turn to me
    and let me heal them.'

Reflect.

Romans

Christ & Culture

INVITED TO GO &TEACH

The Letter to the Romans

The Power of the Gospel
Romans 1

Reflect.

1. What is a bond-servant?

2. Why is it significant that Paul is referring to himself as a bond-servant?

3. Would you consider yourself a bond-servant of Jesus? Why or why not?

4. After studying the book of Acts what is significant about the relationship that Paul has with the group of people that this letter is addressed to? (7)

5. What is significant about verse 8 in light of the mission of God and the history of the churches role in that mission as recorded in the book of Acts?

1 Paul, a bond-servant of Christ Jesus, called as an apostle, set apart for the gospel of God,

2 which He promised beforehand through His prophets in the holy Scriptures, 3 concerning His Son, who was born of a descendant of David according to the flesh, 4 who was declared the Son of God with power by the resurrection from the dead, according to the Spirit of holiness, Jesus Christ our Lord,

5 through whom we have received grace and apostleship to bring about the obedience of faith among all the Gentiles for His name's sake, 6 among whom you also are the called of Jesus Christ;

7 to all who are beloved of God in Rome, called as saints: Grace to you and peace from God our Father and the Lord Jesus Christ.

8 First, I thank my God through Jesus Christ for you all, because your faith is being proclaimed throughout the whole world.

The Power of the Gospel
Romans 1

Reflect.

1. Read verse 16 in five different translations and then write the verse in your own words.

2. Define the Gospel in your own words.

3. Now using only words from other scripture references how does Scripture define the Gospel (cite your references).

4. In your won words, describe what it would look like to live a life that is unashamed of the gospel.

5. Knowing what you do from what is recorded about the life of Paul in the book of Acts how does his life reflect a life that is unashamed of the gospel?

6. How does his life reflect the power of the gospel?

7. Describe what it would take for you to follow the example of Paul and live a life that trusted fully in the power of the Gospel.

9 For God, whom I serve in my spirit in the preaching of the gospel of His Son, is my witness as to how unceasingly I make mention of you,

10 always in my prayers making request, if perhaps now at last by the will of God I may succeed in coming to you.

11 For I long to see you so that I may impart some spiritual gift to you, that you may be established; 12 that is, that I may be encouraged together with you while among you, each of us by the other's faith, both yours and mine.

13 I do not want you to be unaware, brethren, that often I have planned to come to you (and have been prevented so far) so that I may obtain some fruit among you also, even as among the rest of the Gentiles.

14 I am under obligation both to Greeks and to barbarians, both to the wise and to the foolish.

15 So, for my part, I am eager to preach the gospel to you also who are in Rome.

16 For I am not ashamed of the gospel, for it is the power of God for salvation to everyone who believes, to the Jew first and also to the Greek.

17 For in it the righteousness of God is revealed from faith to faith; as it is written, "But the righteous man shall live by faith."

Romans

Romans 1

Reflect

Interact with several translations and some bible study tools to determine the meaning and then write out verse 18 and 19 in your own words.

1. Describe verse 18 in your own words.

2. Describe verse 19 in your own words.

3. According to the doctrine of General Revelation, describe from Scripture how God has revealed Himself through creation.

4. According to the doctrine of General Revelation, describe from sources outside of the Bible how God has revealed Himself through creation.

5. One of the problems with General Revelation is that it was intended for a world that had not been tainted by sin. What are some examples of how sin has caused disintegration to the world as it would have been experienced by Adam and Eve in The Garden of Eden? How does that impact us today?

18 For the wrath of God is revealed from heaven against all ungodliness and unrighteousness of men who suppress the truth in unrighteousness,

19 because that which is known about God is evident within them; for God made it evident to them.

20 For since the creation of the world His invisible attributes, His eternal power and divine nature, have been clearly seen, being understood through what has been made, so that they are without excuse.

6. One of the cultural questions of our generation is whether or not science and scripture agree. Passionate arguments are made on both sides of the issue but from a Theological perspective how could verse 20 help us to make sense of the argument?

7. On the other hand, how could this verse contribute to the confusion?

Romans

Romans 1

Reflect

1. List some examples from the Old Testament that illustrate the truth of verse 21.

2. List some examples from our generation that illustrate the truth of verse 21.

3. In your own words, state the argument for how an individual who approaches Scripture from the perspective that Genesis clearly teaches a non-evolutionary approach to creation understand and apply verses 21, 22, 23 to those who adhere to the theory of macroevolution.

4. Continuing to view this passage from the perspective of an individual who approaches Scripture from the perspective that macroevolution is in contradiction to Genesis, how could this individual use verses 24-25 to connect our modern cultural tension regarding gender identify with the natural outworking of a worldview based on macroevolution?

21 For even though they knew God, they did not honor Him as God or give thanks, but they became futile in their speculations, and their foolish heart was darkened.

22 Professing to be wise, they became fools, 23 and exchanged the glory of the incorruptible God for an image in the form of corruptible man and of birds and four-footed animals and crawling creatures.

24 Therefore God gave them over in the lusts of their hearts to impurity, so that their bodies would be dishonored among them. 25 For they exchanged the truth of God for a lie, and worshiped and served the creature rather than the Creator, who is blessed forever.

Amen.

5. Now take the opposite theological perspective and describe how a Christ-centered Theist who held to a worldview that allowed for Theistic evolution might respond exegetically and Theologically to the descriptions, claims and/or assertions of an individual who held to a literal 6 day reading of Genesis.

6. How would you respond to an argument regarding a connection between these verses and your Theological Perspective?

7. What contextual evidence or cross references would you use?

Romans

Romans 1

26 For this reason God gave them over to degrading passions; for their women exchanged the natural function for that which is unnatural,

27 and in the same way also the men abandoned the natural function of the woman and burned in their desire toward one another, men with men committing indecent acts and receiving in their own persons the due penalty of their error.

28 And just as they did not see fit to acknowledge God any longer, God gave them over to a depraved mind, to do those things which are not proper,

29 being filled with all unrighteousness, wickedness, greed, evil; full of envy, murder, strife, deceit, malice; they are gossips,

30 slanderers, haters of God, insolent, arrogant, boastful, inventors of evil, disobedient to parents,

31 without understanding, untrustworthy, unloving, unmerciful;

32 and although they know the ordinance of God, that those who practice such things are worthy of death, they not only do the same, but also give hearty approval to those who practice them.

Reflect

Paul begins his argument in chapter 1 with a strong defense for the power of the Gospel to change lives. Then he begins to make the case for those who resist the message of the Gospel.

1. In your own words what is the connection and application between verses 26-30 and the struggles, claims and tension within current culture in our generation?

2. What is the meaning of verse 32?

3. What should be the application of verse 32 in the life of a Christ-centered theist?

4. What is the cultural struggle to that application that a Christ-centered theist faces?

5. What should be our response?

Romans

Romans 2

1 Therefore you have no excuse, everyone of you who passes judgment, for in that which you judge another, you condemn yourself; for you who judge practice the same things.

2 And we know that the judgment of God rightly falls upon those who practice such things.

3 But do you suppose this, O man, when you pass judgment on those who practice such things and do the same yourself, that you will escape the judgment of God?

4 Or do you think lightly of the riches of His kindness and tolerance and patience, not knowing that the kindness of God leads you to repentance?

5 But because of your stubbornness and unrepentant heart you are storing up wrath for yourself in the day of wrath and revelation of the righteous judgment of God, 6 who will render to each person according to his deeds:

7 to those who by perseverance in doing good seek for glory and honor and immortality, eternal life;

8 but to those who are selfishly ambitious and do not obey the truth, but obey unrighteousness, wrath and indignation. 9 There will be tribulation and distress for every soul of man who does evil, of the Jew first and also of the Greek,

Reflect

The Roman attitude toward sex and sexuality was approached from a materialistic perspective. Sex was about pleasure and power.

It Roman culture it was expected, acceptable and desirable for Roman men to desire sex with both males and females.

Same sex relationships, group sexual encounters and the freedom for Male Roman Citizens to prey upon young male slaves as demonstrations of power and for the purpose of pleasure were all considered acceptable and within the bounds of cultural norms.

In light of this cultural context that Paul continues his train of thought to those within Rome who are considered believers in Christ and continues his thought and application from verse 32 of the first chapter in the opening verses of chapter 2 as well as revisiting the concepts in 13:12-14.

In your own words, what does 2:1-3 accuse these Christians who are living in Rome of being guilty of?

Go back and revisit Romans 1:8 where Paul begins his letter to these believers in Christ by applauding them for "their faith being proclaimed throughout the world" and compare and contrast that praise with the reality of the accusation in 2:1-3.

Paul then judges not only the actions of the Roman believers but continues his indictment with a judgment of their hearts toward their sin in verse 5.

Use Paul's accusation as an examination of the attitudes of your own heart toward sin.

Are there areas in your life where you are stubborn and unrepentant because you find yourself enjoying your sin more than desiring to obey God?

Reflect on the state of the church in our current generation. If the majority of the church held your current attitude toward sin how might that impact the possibility of the power of God at work through the Gospel of Christ to be reflected in the culture?

Romans

Romans 2

10 but glory and honor and peace to everyone who does good, to the Jew first and also to the Greek.

11 For there is no partiality with God.

12 For all who have sinned without the Law will also perish without the Law, and all who have sinned under the Law will be judged by the Law;

13 for it is not the hearers of the Law who are just before God, but the doers of the Law will be justified.

14 For when Gentiles who do not have the Law do instinctively the things of the Law, these, not having the Law, are a law to themselves,

15 in that they show the work of the Law written in their hearts, their conscience bearing witness and their thoughts alternately accusing or else defending them,

16 on the day when, according to my gospel, God will judge the secrets of men through Christ Jesus.

Reflect

1. Sometimes it is easy to excuse our private actions because of our public persona or behavior. In our minds, our private actions can be excused because our secret sins do not seem to impact anyone else noticeably. Based on what you have read in Romans up to this point how do you think Paul would react to that mindset?

2. Using Paul's words from Romans 1 and 2 how would you counsel someone who was living life from the perspective that their private actions, attitudes, and behaviors were not of any actual consequence and were simply their issues or even non-issues.

3. How does Paul continue to expand and explain his argument in 2:10-15?

4. What is the warning and consequence of verse 16?

5. How would you counsel someone who was wrestling with enjoying the assumed pleasures of sin like the Roman believers were? Why would you take that approach?

6. Do you think your plan as outlined in your response is the typical approach today? Why or why not?

Romans

Romans 2

17 But if you bear the name "Jew" and rely upon the Law and boast in God,

18 and know His will and approve the things that are essential, being instructed out of the Law,

19 and are confident that you yourself are a guide to the blind, a light to those who are in darkness, 20 a corrector of the foolish, a teacher of the immature, having in the Law the embodiment of knowledge and of the truth,

21 you, therefore, who teach another, do you not teach yourself? You who preach that one shall not steal, do you steal?

22 You who say that one should not commit adultery, do you commit adultery? You who abhor idols, do you rob temples? 23 You who boast in the Law, through your breaking the Law, do you dishonor God?
24 For "the name of God is blasphemed among the Gentiles because of you," just as it is written.

25 For indeed circumcision is of value if you practice the Law; but if you are a transgressor of the Law, your circumcision has become uncircumcision. 26 So if the uncircumcised man keeps the requirements of the Law, will not his uncircumcision be regarded as circumcision?

27 And he who is physically uncircumcised, if he keeps the Law, will he not judge you who though having the letter of the Law and circumcision are a transgressor of the Law?

28 For he is not a Jew who is one outwardly, nor is circumcision that which is outward in the flesh.

29 But he is a Jew who is one inwardly; and circumcision is that which is of the heart, by the Spirit, not by the letter; and his praise is not from men, but from God.

Respond.

Reflect.

Romans

Romans 3

3 Then what advantage has the Jew? Or what is the benefit of circumcision? 2 Great in every respect. First of all, that they were entrusted with the oracles of God. 3 What then? If some did not believe, their unbelief will not nullify the faithfulness of God, will it? 4 May it never be! Rather, let God be found true, though every man be found a liar, as it is written,
"That You may be justified in Your words,
And prevail when You are judged."
5 But if our unrighteousness demonstrates the righteousness of God, what shall we say? The God who inflicts wrath is not unrighteous, is He? (I am speaking in human terms.) 6 May it never be! For otherwise, how will God judge the world? 7 But if through my lie the truth of God abounded to His glory, why am I also still being judged as a sinner? 8 And why not say (as we are slanderously reported and as some claim that we say), "Let us do evil that good may come"? Their condemnation is just.
9 What then? Are we better than they? Not at all; for we have already charged that both Jews and Greeks are all under sin; 10 as it is written,
"There is none righteous, not even one;
11 There is none who understands,
There is none who seeks for God;
12 All have turned aside, together they have become useless;
There is none who does good,
There is not even one."
13 "Their throat is an open grave,
With their tongues they keep deceiving,"
"The poison of asps is under their lips";
14 "Whose mouth is full of cursing and bitterness";

15 "Their feet are swift to shed blood,
16 Destruction and misery are in their paths,
17 And the path of peace they have not known."
18 "There is no fear of God before their eyes."
19 Now we know that whatever the Law says, it speaks to those who are under the Law, so that every mouth may be closed and all the world may become accountable to God; 20 because by the works of the Law no flesh will be justified in His sight; for through the Law comes the knowledge of sin.

Justification by Faith

21 But now apart from the Law the righteousness of God has been manifested, being witnessed by the Law and the Prophets, 22 even the righteousness of God through faith in Jesus Christ for all those who believe; for there is no distinction; 23 for all have sinned and fall short of the glory of God, 24 being justified as a gift by His grace through the redemption which is in Christ Jesus; 25 whom God displayed publicly as a propitiation in His blood through faith. This was to demonstrate His righteousness, because in the forbearance of God He passed over the sins previously committed; 26 for the demonstration, I say, of His righteousness at the present time, so that He would be just and the justifier of the one who has faith in Jesus.
27 Where then is boasting? It is excluded. By what kind of law? Of works? No, but by a law of faith. 28 For we maintain that a man is justified by faith apart from works of the Law. 29 Or is God the God of Jews only? Is He not the God of Gentiles also? Yes, of Gentiles also, 30 since indeed God who will justify the circumcised by faith and the uncircumcised through faith is one.
31 Do we then nullify the Law through faith? May it never be! On the contrary, we establish the Law.

Respond.

Reflect.

Romans

Romans 4

4 What then shall we say that Abraham, our forefather according to the flesh, has found? 2 For if Abraham was justified by works, he has something to boast about, but not before God. 3 For what does the Scripture say? "Abraham believed God, and it was credited to him as righteousness." 4 Now to the one who works, his wage is not credited as a favor, but as what is due. 5 But to the one who does not work, but believes in Him who justifies the ungodly, his faith is credited as righteousness, 6 just as David also speaks of the blessing on the man to whom God credits righteousness apart from works:

7 "Blessed are those whose lawless deeds have been forgiven,

And whose sins have been covered.

8 "Blessed is the man whose sin the Lord will not take into account."

9 Is this blessing then on the circumcised, or on the uncircumcised also? For we say, "Faith was credited to Abraham as righteousness." 10 How then was it credited? While he was circumcised, or uncircumcised? Not while circumcised, but while uncircumcised; 11 and he received the sign of circumcision, a seal of the righteousness of the faith which he had while uncircumcised, so that he might be the father of all who believe without being circumcised, that righteousness might be credited to them, 12 and the father of circumcision to those who not only are of the circumcision, but who also follow in the steps of the faith of our father Abraham which he had while uncircumcised.

13 For the promise to Abraham or to his descendants that he would be heir of the world was not through the Law, but through the righteousness of faith. 14 For if those who are of the Law are heirs, faith is made void and the promise is nullified; 15 for the Law brings about wrath, but where there is no law, there also is no violation.

16 For this reason it is by faith, in order that it may be in accordance with grace, so that the promise will be guaranteed to all the descendants, not only to those who are of the Law, but also to those who are of the faith of Abraham, who is the father of us all, 17 (as it is written, "A father of many nations have I made you") in the presence of Him whom he believed, even God, who gives life to the dead and calls into being that which does not exist. 18 In hope against hope he believed, so that he might become a father of many nations according to that which had been spoken, "So shall your descendants be." 19 Without becoming weak in faith he contemplated his own body, now as good as dead since he was about a hundred years old, and the deadness of Sarah's womb; 20 yet, with respect to the promise of God, he did not waver in unbelief but grew strong in faith, giving glory to God, 21 and being fully assured that what God had promised, He was able also to perform. 22 Therefore it was also credited to him as righteousness. 23 Now not for his sake only was it written that it was credited to him, 24 but for our sake also, to whom it will be credited, as those who believe in Him who raised Jesus our Lord from the dead, 25 He who was delivered over because of our transgressions, and was raised because of our justification.

Respond.

Reflect.

Romans

Romans 5

5 Therefore, having been justified by faith, we have peace with God through our Lord Jesus Christ, 2 through whom also we have obtained our introduction by faith into this grace in which we stand; and we exult in hope of the glory of God. 3 And not only this, but we also exult in our tribulations, knowing that tribulation brings about perseverance; 4 and perseverance, proven character; and proven character, hope; 5 and hope does not disappoint, because the love of God has been poured out within our hearts through the Holy Spirit who was given to us.

6 For while we were still helpless, at the right time Christ died for the ungodly. 7 For one will hardly die for a righteous man; though perhaps for the good man someone would dare even to die. 8 But God demonstrates His own love toward us, in that while we were yet sinners, Christ died for us. 9 Much more then, having now been justified by His blood, we shall be saved from the wrath of God through Him. 10 For if while we were enemies we were reconciled to God through the death of His Son, much more, having been reconciled, we shall be saved by His life. 11 And not only this, but we also exult in God through our Lord Jesus Christ, through whom we have now received the reconciliation.

12 Therefore, just as through one man sin entered into the world, and death through sin, and so death spread to all men, because all sinned– 13 for until the Law sin was in the world, but sin is not imputed when there is no law. 14 Nevertheless death reigned from Adam until Moses, even over those who had not sinned in the likeness of the offense of Adam, who is a type of Him who was to come.

15 But the free gift is not like the transgression. For if by the transgression of the one the many died, much more did the grace of God and the gift by the grace of the one Man, Jesus Christ, abound to the many. 16 The gift is not like that which came through the one who sinned; for on the one hand the judgment arose from one transgression resulting in condemnation, but on the other hand the free gift arose from many transgressions resulting in justification. 17 For if by the transgression of the one, death reigned through the one, much more those who receive the abundance of grace and of the gift of righteousness will reign in life through the One, Jesus Christ.

18 So then as through one transgression there resulted condemnation to all men, even so through one act of righteousness there resulted justification of life to all men. 19 For as through the one man's disobedience the many were made sinners, even so through the obedience of the One the many will be made righteous. 20 The Law came in so that the transgression would increase; but where sin increased, grace abounded all the more, 21 so that, as sin reigned in death, even so grace would reign through righteousness to eternal life through Jesus Christ our Lord.

Respond.

Reflect.

Romans

Romans 6

6 What shall we say then? Are we to continue in sin so that grace may increase? 2 May it never be! How shall we who died to sin still live in it? 3 Or do you not know that all of us who have been baptized into Christ Jesus have been baptized into His death? 4 Therefore we have been buried with Him through baptism into death, so that as Christ was raised from the dead through the glory of the Father, so we too might walk in newness of life. 5 For if we have become united with Him in the likeness of His death, certainly we shall also be in the likeness of His resurrection, 6 knowing this, that our old self was crucified with Him, in order that our body of sin might be done away with, so that we would no longer be slaves to sin; 7 for he who has died is freed from sin.

8 Now if we have died with Christ, we believe that we shall also live with Him, 9 knowing that Christ, having been raised from the dead, is never to die again; death no longer is master over Him. 10 For the death that He died, He died to sin once for all; but the life that He lives, He lives to God. 11 Even so consider yourselves to be dead to sin, but alive to God in Christ Jesus.

12 Therefore do not let sin reign in your mortal body so that you obey its lusts, 13 and do not go on presenting the members of your body to sin as instruments of unrighteousness; but present yourselves to God as those alive from the dead, and your members as instruments of righteousness to God. 14 For sin shall not be master over you, for you are not under law but under grace.

15 What then? Shall we sin because we are not under law but under grace? May it never be! 16 Do you not know that when you present yourselves to someone as slaves for obedience, you are slaves of the one whom you obey, either of sin resulting in death, or of obedience resulting in righteousness? 17 But thanks be to God that though you were slaves of sin, you became obedient from the heart to that form of teaching to which you were committed, 18 and having been freed from sin, you became slaves of righteousness. 19 I am speaking in human terms because of the weakness of your flesh. For just as you presented your members as slaves to impurity and to lawlessness, resulting in further lawlessness, so now present your members as slaves to righteousness, resulting in sanctification.

20 For when you were slaves of sin, you were free in regard to righteousness. 21 Therefore what benefit were you then deriving from the things of which you are now ashamed? For the outcome of those things is death. 22 But now having been freed from sin and enslaved to God, you derive your benefit, resulting in sanctification, and the outcome, eternal life. 23 For the wages of sin is death, but the free gift of God is eternal life in Christ Jesus our Lord.

Respond.

Reflect.

Romans

Romans 7

7 Or do you not know, brethren (for I am speaking to those who know the law), that the law has jurisdiction over a person as long as he lives? 2 For the married woman is bound by law to her husband while he is living; but if her husband dies, she is released from the law concerning the husband. 3 So then, if while her husband is living she is joined to another man, she shall be called an adulteress; but if her husband dies, she is free from the law, so that she is not an adulteress though she is joined to another man.

4 Therefore, my brethren, you also were made to die to the Law through the body of Christ, so that you might be joined to another, to Him who was raised from the dead, in order that we might bear fruit for God. 5 For while we were in the flesh, the sinful passions, which were aroused by the Law, were at work in the members of our body to bear fruit for death. 6 But now we have been released from the Law, having died to that by which we were bound, so that we serve in newness of the Spirit and not in oldness of the letter.

7 What shall we say then? Is the Law sin? May it never be! On the contrary, I would not have come to know sin except through the Law; for I would not have known about coveting if the Law had not said, "You shall not covet." 8 But sin, taking opportunity through the commandment, produced in me coveting of every kind; for apart from the Law sin is dead. 9 I was once alive apart from the Law; but when the commandment came, sin became alive and I died; 10 and this commandment, which was to result in life, proved to result in death for me; 11 for sin, taking an opportunity through the commandment, deceived me and through it killed me. 12 So then, the Law is holy, and the commandment is holy and righteous and good.

13 Therefore did that which is good become a cause of death for me? May it never be! Rather it was sin, in order that it might be shown to be sin by effecting my death through that which is good, so that through the commandment sin would become utterly sinful.

The Conflict of Two Natures

14 For we know that the Law is spiritual, but I am of flesh, sold into bondage to sin. 15 For what I am doing, I do not understand; for I am not practicing what I would like to do, but I am doing the very thing I hate. 16 But if I do the very thing I do not want to do, I agree with the Law, confessing that the Law is good. 17 So now, no longer am I the one doing it, but sin which dwells in me. 18 For I know that nothing good dwells in me, that is, in my flesh; for the willing is present in me, but the doing of the good is not. 19 For the good that I want, I do not do, but I practice the very evil that I do not want. 20 But if I am doing the very thing I do not want, I am no longer the one doing it, but sin which dwells in me.

21 I find then the principle that evil is present in me, the one who wants to do good. 22 For I joyfully concur with the law of God in the inner man, 23 but I see a different law in the members of my body, waging war against the law of my mind and making me a prisoner of the law of sin which is in my members. 24 Wretched man that I am! Who will set me free from the body of this death? 25 Thanks be to God through Jesus Christ our Lord! So then, on the one hand I myself with my mind am serving the law of God, but on the other, with my flesh the law of sin.

Romans
Romans 8

8 Therefore there is now no condemnation for those who are in Christ Jesus. 2 For the law of the Spirit of life in Christ Jesus has set you free from the law of sin and of death. 3 For what the Law could not do, weak as it was through the flesh, God did: sending His own Son in the likeness of sinful flesh and as an offering for sin, He condemned sin in the flesh, 4 so that the requirement of the Law might be fulfilled in us, who do not walk according to the flesh but according to the Spirit. 5 For those who are according to the flesh set their minds on the things of the flesh, but those who are according to the Spirit, the things of the Spirit. 6 For the mind set on the flesh is death, but the mind set on the Spirit is life and peace, 7 because the mind set on the flesh is hostile toward God; for it does not subject itself to the law of God, for it is not even able to do so, 8 and those who are in the flesh cannot please God.

9 However, you are not in the flesh but in the Spirit, if indeed the Spirit of God dwells in you. But if anyone does not have the Spirit of Christ, he does not belong to Him. 10 If Christ is in you, though the body is dead because of sin, yet the spirit is alive because of righteousness. 11 But if the Spirit of Him who raised Jesus from the dead dwells in you, He who raised Christ Jesus from the dead will also give life to your mortal bodies through His Spirit who dwells in you.

12 So then, brethren, we are under obligation, not to the flesh, to live according to the flesh— 13 for if you are living according to the flesh, you must die; but if by the Spirit you are putting to death the deeds of the body, you will live.

Respond.

14 For all who are being led by the Spirit of God, these are sons of God. 15 For you have not received a spirit of slavery leading to fear again, but you have received a spirit of adoption as sons by which we cry out, "Abba! Father!" 16 The Spirit Himself testifies with our spirit that we are children of God, 17 and if children, heirs also, heirs of God and fellow heirs with Christ, if indeed we suffer with Him so that we may also be glorified with Him.

18 For I consider that the sufferings of this present time are not worthy to be compared with the glory that is to be revealed to us. 19 For the anxious longing of the creation waits eagerly for the revealing of the sons of God. 20 For the creation was subjected to futility, not willingly, but because of Him who subjected it, in hope 21 that the creation itself also will be set free from its slavery to corruption into the freedom of the glory of the children of God. 22 For we know that the whole creation groans and suffers the pains of childbirth together until now. 23 And not only this, but also we ourselves, having the first fruits of the Spirit, even we ourselves groan within ourselves, waiting eagerly for our adoption as sons, the redemption of our body. 24 For in hope we have been saved, but hope that is seen is not hope; for who hopes for what he already sees? 25 But if we hope for what we do not see, with perseverance we wait eagerly for it.

Reflect.

Romans

Romans 8-9

26 In the same way the Spirit also helps our weakness; for we do not know how to pray as we should, but the Spirit Himself intercedes for us with groanings too deep for words; 27 and He who searches the hearts knows what the mind of the Spirit is, because He intercedes for the saints according to the will of God.

28 And we know that God causes all things to work together for good to those who love God, to those who are called according to His purpose. 29 For those whom He foreknew, He also predestined to become conformed to the image of His Son, so that He would be the firstborn among many brethren; 30 and these whom He predestined, He also called; and these whom He called, He also justified; and these whom He justified, He also glorified.

31 What then shall we say to these things? If God is for us, who is against us? 32 He who did not spare His own Son, but delivered Him over for us all, how will He not also with Him freely give us all things? 33 Who will bring a charge against God's elect? God is the one who justifies; 34 who is the one who condemns? Christ Jesus is He who died, yes, rather who was raised, who is at the right hand of God, who also intercedes for us.

35 Who will separate us from the love of Christ? Will tribulation, or distress, or persecution, or famine, or nakedness, or peril, or sword? 36 Just as it is written,

> "For Your sake we are being put to death all day long; We were considered as sheep to be slaughtered."

37 But in all these things we overwhelmingly conquer through Him who loved us. 38 For I am convinced that neither death, nor life, nor angels, nor principalities, nor things present, nor things to come, nor powers, 39 nor height, nor depth, nor any other created thing, will be able to separate us from the love of God, which is in Christ Jesus our Lord.

Respond.

Reflect.

Romans
Romans 9

9 I am telling the truth in Christ, I am not lying, my conscience testifies with me in the Holy Spirit, 2 that I have great sorrow and unceasing grief in my heart. 3 For I could wish that I myself were accursed, separated from Christ for the sake of my brethren, my kinsmen according to the flesh, 4 who are Israelites, to whom belongs the adoption as sons, and the glory and the covenants and the giving of the Law and the temple service and the promises, 5 whose are the fathers, and from whom is the Christ according to the flesh, who is over all, God blessed forever. Amen.

6 But it is not as though the word of God has failed. For they are not all Israel who are descended from Israel; 7 nor are they all children because they are Abraham's descendants, but: "through Isaac your descendants will be named."

8 That is, it is not the children of the flesh who are children of God, but the children of the promise are regarded as descendants. 9 For this is the word of promise: "At this time I will come, and Sarah shall have a son." 10 And not only this, but there was Rebekah also, when she had conceived twins by one man, our father Isaac;

11 for though the twins were not yet born and had not done anything good or bad, so that God's purpose according to His choice would stand, not because of works but because of Him who calls, 12 it was said to her, "The older will serve the younger." 13 Just as it is written, "Jacob I loved, but Esau I hated."

14 What shall we say then? There is no injustice with God, is there? May it never be!

15 For He says to Moses, "I will have mercy on whom I have mercy, and I will have compassion on whom I have compassion." 16 So then it does not depend on the man who wills or the man who runs, but on God who has mercy.

Respond.

Reflect.

Romans
Romans 9

Respond.

Reflect.

17 For the Scripture says to Pharaoh, "For this very purpose I raised you up, to demonstrate My power in you, and that My name might be proclaimed throughout the whole earth." 18 So then He has mercy on whom He desires, and He hardens whom He desires.

19 You will say to me then, "Why does He still find fault? For who resists His will?"

20 On the contrary, who are you, O man, who answers back to God? The thing molded will not say to the molder, "Why did you make me like this," will it?

21 Or does not the potter have a right over the clay, to make from the same lump one vessel for honorable use and another for common use?

22 What if God, although willing to demonstrate His wrath and to make His power known, endured with much patience vessels of wrath prepared for destruction? 23 And He did so to make known the riches of His glory upon vessels of mercy, which He prepared beforehand for glory, 24 even us, whom He also called, not from among Jews only, but also from among Gentiles.

25 As He says also in Hosea,

> "I will call those who were not My people, 'My people,' And her who was not beloved, 'beloved.'"
> 26 "And it shall be that in the place where it was said to them, 'you are not My people,' There they shall be called sons of the living God."

Romans

Romans 9

27 Isaiah cries out concerning Israel, "Though the number of the sons of Israel be like the sand of the sea, it is the remnant that will be saved; 28 for the Lord will execute His word on the earth, thoroughly and quickly." 29 And just as Isaiah foretold, "Unless the Lord of Sabaoth had left to us a posterity, We would have become like Sodom, and would have resembled Gomorrah."

30 What shall we say then? That Gentiles, who did not pursue righteousness, attained righteousness, even the righteousness which is by faith; 31 but Israel, pursuing a law of righteousness, did not arrive at that law.

32 Why?

Because they did not pursue it by faith, but as though it were by works. They stumbled over the stumbling stone, 33 just as it is written,

> "Behold, I lay in Zion a stone of stumbling and a rock of offense, And he who believes in Him will not be disappointed."

Respond.

Reflect.

Romans

Romans 10-11:6

10 Brethren, my heart's desire and my prayer to God for them is for their salvation. 2 For I testify about them that they have a zeal for God, but not in accordance with knowledge. 3 For not knowing about God's righteousness and seeking to establish their own, they did not subject themselves to the righteousness of God. 4 For Christ is the end of the law for righteousness to everyone who believes.

5 For Moses writes that the man who practices the righteousness which is based on law shall live by that righteousness. 6 But the righteousness based on faith speaks as follows: "Do not say in your heart, 'Who will ascend into heaven?' (that is, to bring Christ down), 7 or 'Who will descend into the abyss?' (that is, to bring Christ up from the dead)."

8 But what does it say? "The word is near you, in your mouth and in your heart"–that is, the word of faith which we are preaching, 9 that if you confess with your mouth Jesus as Lord, and believe in your heart that God raised Him from the dead, you will be saved; 10 for with the heart a person believes, resulting in righteousness, and with the mouth he confesses, resulting in salvation. 11 For the Scripture says, "Whoever believes in Him will not be disappointed."

12 For there is no distinction between Jew and Greek; for the same Lord is Lord of all, abounding in riches for all who call on Him; 13 for "Whoever will call on the name of the Lord will be saved."

14 How then will they call on Him in whom they have not believed? How will they believe in Him whom they have not heard? And how will they hear without a preacher? 15 How will they preach unless they are sent? Just as it is written, "How beautiful are the feet of those who bring good news of good things!"

Respond.

Reflect.

Romans
Romans 10-11:6

Respond.

Reflect.

16 However, they did not all heed the good news; for Isaiah says, "Lord, who has believed our report?" 17 So faith comes from hearing, and hearing by the word of Christ.

18 But I say, surely they have never heard, have they? Indeed they have; "Their voice has gone out into all the earth, And their words to the ends of the world."

19 But I say, surely Israel did not know, did they?

First Moses says, "I will make you jealous by that which is not a nation, By a nation without understanding will I anger you."

20 And Isaiah is very bold and says, "I was found by those who did not seek Me, I became manifest to those who did not ask for Me."

21 But as for Israel He says, "All the day long I have stretched out My hands to a disobedient and obstinate people."

11:1 I say then, God has not rejected His people, has He? May it never be! For I too am an Israelite, a descendant of Abraham, of the tribe of Benjamin.

2 God has not rejected His people whom He foreknew. Or do you not know what the Scripture says in the passage about Elijah, how he pleads with God against Israel? 3 "Lord, they have killed Your prophets, they have torn down Your altars, and I alone am left, and they are seeking my life."

4 But what is the divine response to him? "I have kept for Myself seven thousand men who have not bowed the knee to Baal." 5 In the same way then, there has also come to be at the present time a remnant according to God's gracious choice. 6 But if it is by grace, it is no longer on the basis of works, otherwise grace is no longer grace.

Romans

Romans 11

11 I say then, God has not rejected His people, has He? May it never be! For I too am an Israelite, a descendant of Abraham, of the tribe of Benjamin.

2 God has not rejected His people whom He foreknew. Or do you not know what the Scripture says in the passage about Elijah, how he pleads with God against Israel? 3 "Lord, they have killed Your prophets, they have torn down Your altars, and I alone am left, and they are seeking my life."

4 But what is the divine response to him? "I have kept for Myself seven thousand men who have not bowed the knee to Baal." 5 In the same way then, there has also come to be at the present time a remnant according to God's gracious choice. 6 But if it is by grace, it is no longer on the basis of works, otherwise grace is no longer grace.

7 What then? What Israel is seeking, it has not obtained, but those who were chosen obtained it, and the rest were hardened; 8 just as it is written,

> "God gave them a spirit of stupor,
> Eyes to see not and ears to hear not,
> Down to this very day."

9 And David says,

> "Let their table become a snare and a trap, And a stumbling block and a retribution to them.
> 10 "Let their eyes be darkened to see not, And bend their backs forever."

Respond.

Reflect.

Romans

Romans 11

11 I say then, they did not stumble so as to fall, did they? May it never be! But by their transgression salvation has come to the Gentiles, to make them jealous.

12 Now if their transgression is riches for the world and their failure is riches for the Gentiles, how much more will their fulfillment be! 13 But I am speaking to you who are Gentiles. Inasmuch then as I am an apostle of Gentiles, I magnify my ministry, 14 if somehow I might move to jealousy my fellow countrymen and save some of them. 15 For if their rejection is the reconciliation of the world, what will their acceptance be but life from the dead? 16 If the first piece of dough is holy, the lump is also; and if the root is holy, the branches are too.

17 But if some of the branches were broken off, and you, being a wild olive, were grafted in among them and became partaker with them of the rich root of the olive tree, 18 do not be arrogant toward the branches; but if you are arrogant, remember that it is not you who supports the root, but the root supports you. 19 You will say then, "Branches were broken off so that I might be grafted in."

20 Quite right, they were broken off for their unbelief, but you stand by your faith. Do not be conceited, but fear; 21 for if God did not spare the natural branches, He will not spare you, either. 22 Behold then the kindness and severity of God; to those who fell, severity, but to you, God's kindness, if you continue in His kindness; otherwise you also will be cut off. 23 And they also, if they do not continue in their unbelief, will be grafted in, for God is able to graft them in again.

Respond.

24 For if you were cut off from what is by nature a wild olive tree, and were grafted contrary to nature into a cultivated olive tree, how much more will these who are the natural branches be grafted into their own olive tree? 25 For I do not want you, brethren, to be uninformed of this mystery–so that you will not be wise in your own estimation–that a partial hardening has happened to Israel until the fullness of the Gentiles has come in; 26 and so all Israel will be saved; just as it is written,
"The Deliverer will come from Zion,
He will remove ungodliness from Jacob."
27
"This is My covenant with them,
When I take away their sins."
28 From the standpoint of the gospel they are enemies for your sake, but from the standpoint of God's choice they are beloved for the sake of the fathers; 29 for the gifts and the calling of God are irrevocable. 30 For just as you once were disobedient to God, but now have been shown mercy because of their disobedience, 31 so these also now have been disobedient, that because of the mercy shown to you they also may now be shown mercy. 32 For God has shut up all in disobedience so that He may show mercy to all.
33 Oh, the depth of the riches both of the wisdom and knowledge of God! How unsearchable are His judgments and unfathomable His ways! 34 For who has known the mind of the Lord, or who became His counselor? 35 Or who has first given to Him that it might be paid back to him again? 36 For from Him and through Him and to Him are all things. To Him be the glory forever. Amen.

Reflect.

Romans

Romans 12

12 Therefore I urge you, brethren, by the mercies of God, to present your bodies a living and holy sacrifice, acceptable to God, which is your spiritual service of worship. 2 And do not be conformed to this world, but be transformed by the renewing of your mind, so that you may prove what the will of God is, that which is good and acceptable and perfect.

3 For through the grace given to me I say to everyone among you not to think more highly of himself than he ought to think; but to think so as to have sound judgment, as God has allotted to each a measure of faith. 4 For just as we have many members in one body and all the members do not have the same function, 5 so we, who are many, are one body in Christ, and individually members one of another. 6 Since we have gifts that differ according to the grace given to us, each of us is to exercise them accordingly: if prophecy, according to the proportion of his faith; 7 if service, in his serving; or he who teaches, in his teaching; 8 or he who exhorts, in his exhortation; he who gives, with liberality; he who leads, with diligence; he who shows mercy, with cheerfulness.

9 Let love be without hypocrisy. Abhor what is evil; cling to what is good. 10 Be devoted to one another in brotherly love; give preference to one another in honor; 11 not lagging behind in diligence, fervent in spirit, serving the Lord; 12 rejoicing in hope, persevering in tribulation, devoted to prayer, 13 contributing to the needs of the saints, practicing hospitality.

14 Bless those who persecute you; bless and do not curse. 15 Rejoice with those who rejoice, and weep with those who weep. 16 Be of the same mind toward one another; do not be haughty in mind, but associate with the lowly. Do not be wise in your own estimation. 17 Never pay back evil for evil to anyone. Respect what is right in the sight of all men. 18 If possible, so far as it depends on you, be at peace with all men. 19 Never take your own revenge, beloved, but leave room for the wrath of God, for it is written, "Vengeance is Mine, I will repay," says the Lord. 20 "But if your enemy is hungry, feed him, and if he is thirsty, give him a drink; for in so doing you will heap burning coals on his head." 21 Do not be overcome by evil, but overcome evil with good.

Respond.

Reflect.

Romans

Romans 13

13 Every person is to be in subjection to the governing authorities. For there is no authority except from God, and those which exist are established by God. 2 Therefore whoever resists authority has opposed the ordinance of God; and they who have opposed will receive condemnation upon themselves. 3 For rulers are not a cause of fear for good behavior, but for evil. Do you want to have no fear of authority? Do what is good and you will have praise from the same; 4 for it is a minister of God to you for good. But if you do what is evil, be afraid; for it does not bear the sword for nothing; for it is a minister of God, an avenger who brings wrath on the one who practices evil. 5 Therefore it is necessary to be in subjection, not only because of wrath, but also for conscience' sake. 6 For because of this you also pay taxes, for rulers are servants of God, devoting themselves to this very thing. 7 Render to all what is due them: tax to whom tax is due; custom to whom custom; fear to whom fear; honor to whom honor.

8 Owe nothing to anyone except to love one another; for he who loves his neighbor has fulfilled the law. 9 For this, "You shall not commit adultery, You shall not murder, You shall not steal, You shall not covet," and if there is any other commandment, it is summed up in this saying, "You shall love your neighbor as yourself." 10 Love does no wrong to a neighbor; therefore love is the fulfillment of the law.
11 Do this, knowing the time, that it is already the hour for you to awaken from sleep; for now salvation is nearer to us than when we believed. 12 The night is almost gone, and the day is near. Therefore let us lay aside the deeds of darkness and put on the armor of light. 13 Let us behave properly as in the day, not in carousing and drunkenness, not in sexual promiscuity and sensuality, not in strife and jealousy. 14 But put on the Lord Jesus Christ, and make no provision for the flesh in regard to its lusts.

Reflect.

1. Roman Government Officials at the time of Paul's letter to the church in Rome was noted for being excessively corrupt and perverse. In light of that what makes Paul's admonition in chapter 13 counter-cultural?

2. How do you think the members of the Roman church who were subject to torture, persecution, rape and the abuse of authority been tempted to respond to the instruction of Paul?

3. How would adherence to Paul's instruction been a demonstration of the power of the Gospel at work in the life of believers?

4. What is the application to our generation in our current cultural setting? Do you think we have it easier or harder than those who would have initially received this letter from Paul? Explain your response?

5. In light of Romans 13, what questions would you like to ask Paul?

6. In view of Romans 13, what questions would you want to ask the church in Rome at the time this was written?

Romans

Romans 14

14 Now accept the one who is weak in faith, but not for the purpose of passing judgment on his opinions. 2 One person has faith that he may eat all things, but he who is weak eats vegetables only. 3 The one who eats is not to regard with contempt the one who does not eat, and the one who does not eat is not to judge the one who eats, for God has accepted him. 4 Who are you to judge the servant of another? To his own master he stands or falls; and he will stand, for the Lord is able to make him stand.

5 One person regards one day above another, another regards every day alike. Each person must be fully convinced in his own mind. 6 He who observes the day, observes it for the Lord, and he who eats, does so for the Lord, for he gives thanks to God; and he who eats not, for the Lord he does not eat, and gives thanks to God. 7 For not one of us lives for himself, and not one dies for himself; 8 for if we live, we live for the Lord, or if we die, we die for the Lord; therefore whether we live or die, we are the Lord's. 9 For to this end Christ died and lived again, that He might be Lord both of the dead and of the living.

10 But you, why do you judge your brother? Or you again, why do you regard your brother with contempt? For we will all stand before the judgment seat of God. 11 For it is written,
"As I live, says the Lord, every knee shall bow to Me,
And every tongue shall give praise to God."
12 So then each one of us will give an account of himself to God

13 Therefore let us not judge one another anymore, but rather determine this—not to put an obstacle or a stumbling block in a brother's way. 14 I know and am convinced in the Lord Jesus that nothing is unclean in itself; but to him who thinks anything to be unclean, to him it is unclean. 15 For if because of food your brother is hurt, you are no longer walking according to love. Do not destroy with your food him for whom Christ died. 16 Therefore do not let what is for you a good thing be spoken of as evil; 17 for the kingdom of God is not eating and drinking, but righteousness and peace and joy in the Holy Spirit. 18 For he who in this way serves Christ is acceptable to God and approved by men. 19 So then we pursue the things which make for peace and the building up of one another. 20 Do not tear down the work of God for the sake of food. All things indeed are clean, but they are evil for the man who eats and gives offense. 21 It is good not to eat meat or to drink wine, or to do anything by which your brother stumbles. 22 The faith which you have, have as your own conviction before God. Happy is he who does not condemn himself in what he approves. 23 But he who doubts is condemned if he eats, because his eating is not from faith; and whatever is not from faith is sin.

Respond.

Reflect.

.

Romans

Romans 15

15 Now we who are strong ought to bear the weaknesses of those without strength and not just please ourselves. 2 Each of us is to please his neighbor for his good, to his edification. 3 For even Christ did not please Himself; but as it is written, "The reproaches of those who reproached You fell on Me." 4 For whatever was written in earlier times was written for our instruction, so that through perseverance and the encouragement of the Scriptures we might have hope. 5 Now may the God who gives perseverance and encouragement grant you to be of the same mind with one another according to Christ Jesus, 6 so that with one accord you may with one voice glorify the God and Father of our Lord Jesus Christ.

7 Therefore, accept one another, just as Christ also accepted us to the glory of God. 8 For I say that Christ has become a servant to the circumcision on behalf of the truth of God to confirm the promises given to the fathers, 9 and for the Gentiles to glorify God for His mercy; as it is written,
"Therefore I will give praise to You among the Gentiles, And I will sing to Your name."
10 Again he says, "Rejoice, O Gentiles, with His people."
11 And again, "Praise the Lord all you Gentiles, And let all the peoples praise Him."
12 Again Isaiah says, "There shall come the root of Jesse, And He who arises to rule over the Gentiles, In Him shall the Gentiles hope."
13 Now may the God of hope fill you with all joy and peace in believing, so that you will abound in hope by the power of the Holy Spirit.
14 And concerning you, my brethren, I myself also am convinced that you yourselves are full of goodness, filled with all knowledge and able also to admonish one another. 15 But I have written very boldly to you on some points so as to remind you again, because of the grace that was given me from God, 16 to be a minister of Christ Jesus to the Gentiles, ministering as a priest the gospel of God, so that my offering of the Gentiles may become acceptable, sanctified by the Holy Spirit.

17 Therefore in Christ Jesus I have found reason for boasting in things pertaining to God. 18 For I will not presume to speak of anything except what Christ has accomplished through me, resulting in the obedience of the Gentiles by word and deed, 19 in the power of signs and wonders, in the power of the Spirit; so that from Jerusalem and round about as far as Illyricum I have fully preached the gospel of Christ. 20 And thus I aspired to preach the gospel, not where Christ was already named, so that I would not build on another man's foundation; 21 but as it is written,
"They who had no news of Him shall see, And they who have not heard shall understand."
22 For this reason I have often been prevented from coming to you; 23 but now, with no further place for me in these regions, and since I have had for many years a longing to come to you 24 whenever I go to Spain—for I hope to see you in passing, and to be helped on my way there by you, when I have first enjoyed your company for a while— 25 but now, I am going to Jerusalem serving the saints. 26 For Macedonia and Achaia have been pleased to make a contribution for the poor among the saints in Jerusalem. 27 Yes, they were pleased to do so, and they are indebted to them. For if the Gentiles have shared in their spiritual things, they are indebted to minister to them also in material things. 28 Therefore, when I have finished this, and have put my seal on this fruit of theirs, I will go on by way of you to Spain. 29 I know that when I come to you, I will come in the fullness of the blessing of Christ.

30 Now I urge you, brethren, by our Lord Jesus Christ and by the love of the Spirit, to strive together with me in your prayers to God for me, 31 that I may be rescued from those who are disobedient in Judea, and that my service for Jerusalem may prove acceptable to the saints; 32 so that I may come to you in joy by the will of God and find refreshing rest in your company. 33 Now the God of peace be with you all. Amen.

How will I respond?

Christ & Culture
INVITED TO GO &TEACH

Romans

Romans 16

16 I commend to you our sister Phoebe, who is a servant of the church which is at Cenchrea; 2 that you receive her in the Lord in a manner worthy of the saints, and that you help her in whatever matter she may have need of you; for she herself has also been a helper of many, and of myself as well.

3 Greet Prisca and Aquila, my fellow workers in Christ Jesus, 4 who for my life risked their own necks, to whom not only do I give thanks, but also all the churches of the Gentiles; 5 also greet the church that is in their house. Greet Epaenetus, my beloved, who is the first convert to Christ from Asia. 6 Greet Mary, who has worked hard for you. 7 Greet Andronicus and Junias, my kinsmen and my fellow prisoners, who are outstanding among the apostles, who also were in Christ before me. 8 Greet Ampliatus, my beloved in the Lord. 9 Greet Urbanus, our fellow worker in Christ, and Stachys my beloved. 10 Greet Apelles, the approved in Christ. Greet those who are of the household of Aristobulus. 11 Greet Herodion, my kinsman. Greet those of the household of Narcissus, who are in the Lord. 12 Greet Tryphaena and Tryphosa, workers in the Lord. Greet Persis the beloved, who has worked hard in the Lord. 13 Greet Rufus, a choice man in the Lord, also his mother and mine. 14 Greet Asyncritus, Phlegon, Hermes, Patrobas, Hermas and the brethren with them. 15 Greet Philologus and Julia, Nereus and his sister, and Olympas, and all the saints who are with them. 16 Greet one another with a holy kiss. All the churches of Christ greet you.

17 Now I urge you, brethren, keep your eye on those who cause dissensions and hindrances contrary to the teaching which you learned, and turn away from them. 18 For such men are slaves, not of our Lord Christ but of their own appetites; and by their smooth and flattering speech they deceive the hearts of the unsuspecting. 19 For the report of your obedience has reached to all; therefore I am rejoicing over you, but I want you to be wise in what is good and innocent in what is evil. 20 The God of peace will soon crush Satan under your feet.

The grace of our Lord Jesus be with you.

21 Timothy my fellow worker greets you, and so do Lucius and Jason and Sosipater, my kinsmen.

22 I, Tertius, who write this letter, greet you in the Lord.

23 Gaius, host to me and to the whole church, greets you. Erastus, the city treasurer greets you, and Quartus, the brother. 24 [The grace of our Lord Jesus Christ be with you all. Amen.]

25 Now to Him who is able to establish you according to my gospel and the preaching of Jesus Christ, according to the revelation of the mystery which has been kept secret for long ages past, 26 but now is manifested, and by the Scriptures of the prophets, according to the commandment of the eternal God, has been made known to all the nations, leading to obedience of faith; 27 to the only wise God, through Jesus Christ, be the glory forever. Amen.

Respond.

Reflect.

Lingering at the door
Romans 16

Sacred Moments and Last Words

It is funny to consider what memories stay with us and which ones fade over time. Certain memories, some albeit random, seem to reappear from time to time while others stay with us for a lifetime.

Near the end of the first semester of my 9th-grade year in High School, I competed in a speech competition where I had memorized a speech given by the actor Alan Alda at his daughters' college commencement. Now, decades later, his speech which is known as the 62nd Commencement Speech at Connecticut College is still considered one of the top 5 commencement speeches of all time.

Near the beginning of the speech, Alda makes the life observation that the best things said in life typically come last. He states that "people will talk for hours saying nothing much but then linger at the door with words that come with a rush from the heart."

In many ways, Romans 16 is Paul's "rush from the heart" to the church in Rome, and it is a fitting way to bring this class and this curriculum to a close as well.

For those taking this course as a second-semester senior, you are now near the door of transition called graduation. Four years ago you embarked on a journey. A journey that was as spiritual as it was physical, emotional, relational and mental.

As 9th grade students, you were presented with information designed to help you build a foundation of trust for the faith you were invited to receive.

You were challenged to examine the difference between faith and fantasy.
You examined the concepts of reality and truth. And you were invited to view the world through the eyes of those who saw the world differently.

Then you were invited to examine the law of non-contradiction to see whether or not it was possible for everything to be true or if an actual standard for truth existed or if it was possible for every view of the world to be equally true.

If a standard existed, then you were invited to consider who (or what) was the author of that standard. If a standard for truth existed, we were challenged to wrestle with the existence of a truth giver (or God) who would have been the author of the standard. Finally, this author of truth would have needed to reveal the truth to us for us to become aware of its existence in the first place.

Through each of the movements in the years that followed you have been challenged to examine both your relationship with and proximity to the mission of this God who exists and desires to reveal Himself to us in a personal relationship.

Through the book of Romans, Paul has invited the believers in Rome into a similar journey an now in the final chapter he concludes his letter by urging his brothers and sisters in Christ to be on the alert for those whose teaching is contrary to what they have learned. He desires that people are wise and aware of those who have a desire to cause dissension and who will hinder the disciples from completing their mission to bring the reflection of God's glory to the ends of the earth.
Paul warns the disciples of smooth-talking charlatans who will use flattery to deceive the hearts of those who are on the mission with God.

Paul urges the use of wisdom to discern motives and a radar programmed with an early warning device to keep them innocent in their next steps.

Innocent of evil

Over the past 20-year of ministry, I have sent and watch graduates move out into the world. Many seemingly taking their first steps outside of the protective bubbles of Christian schools, classrooms, and friends into a world that often includes the types
of evil that lurk in the dark corners of life.

More recently, I have also found myself in the role that Alda spoke about in his love letter to his daughter when my wife and I sent our oldest daughter out of the safety of our local bubble to reflect Christ in her new circles of influence on the other side of the world.

Lingering at the door
Romans 16

As a result, I have a lot more compassion, empathy and potentially even new insight into the admonitions of both Alda and Paul as they spoke final words into the lives of their physical and spiritual children during a time of life transition.

Now, as you embark into the next steps of your own journey to reflect Christ into your own new circles of influence that He is entrusting to you my prayer for you is that you is to identify a few things that you will keep, leave and expect as you move forward.

Things to keep

First, I pray that you will keep on the mission.

As Paul writes in Romans 16, you will need to be diligent in your focus because life is full of invitations and temptations to deviate from the mission of God. Even throughout the pages of Scripture the percentage of people who knowingly finished well and on the mission with God is low.

Living life on God's mission is counter to the culture we were born into.

You will be continuously invited to inch away from a Christ-centered mission to a conventional self-centered mission in ways that seem enticing, desirable and even beneficial.

One of the greatest gifts that you can give to yourself during this season of transition is to form a covenant between yourself and God in each of the areas where you want to stay committed. Ask God to show you the non-negotiable items in your life that will lead you to become the person He is calling you to be and then accept the reality that you will be tempted throughout the next 5-25 years to give up each one.

Living in this truth of temptation to give up on what we hold and value the closest is what led Jesus to inform Peter prior to the time of prayer in the Garden, that he had prayed that Peter's strength would not fail in the face of temptation (Luke 22:32).

Second, I pray that you will keep alert.

As part of my military training, our Drill Sergeant would call out the words, "Stay Alert!" And our response was to return with "Stay Alive! Drill Sergeant! Stay Alive!"

Approximately four separate times in the New Testament we are exhorted to stay alert in order to stay alive!

In his letter to the Ephesians, Paul writes that as part of our persistence in prayer for believers everywhere we are to "stay alert" as we pray in the Spirit at all times and on every occasion (6:18).

In the same way, Peter exhorts believers to "stay alert" and to watch out for our great enemy who prowls about like a lion looking for prey to devour (1 Peter 5:8).

Both passages contain admonitions toward perseverance; humility and they hold the concept of resting in God's sovereignty in the midst of adversity.

The only way to stay alert in this manner is to daily cultivate your relationship with Jesus. Don't "do devotions" as an act of religious experience. Continue to build into your relationship with Jesus through an increased love and understanding of His revelation through the Word of God.

A quick word study on the term "stand firm" in the New Testament will reveal that those words are always closely related to our relationship to the Word of God. When we are close to the Word of God, we stand firm. When we are far from the Word of God, we risk being on shaky ground with an unsecured foundation in the midst of the storms of life.

As you stay alert, there will be times of trial, testing and even temptation but continue to "stand firm" with your feet solidly planted in the yoke and teaching of Christ under the strength and power of God and His Spirit (Luke 6:48, 1 Corinthians 16:13, 2 Corinthians 1:21, Ephesians 6:11, Colossians 1:23, 2 Thessalonians 2:15, 2 Timothy 2:19).

Lingering at the door
Romans 16

Third, I pray that you will keep free from the distractions and the entanglements of sin.

Sin has a way of enticing us with promises that it can never deliver upon.
It invites us to participate in something with the false promise that we are free to leave at any time only for us to discover later that we have become bound or entangled in something that has gained a level of control over us.

Recently, I heard a local pastor speak at one of our school chapels where he put into words a truth that I can bear witness to the reality of in my own experience as a pastor for 13 years.

He said that much of his time as a pastor was spent counseling people in their thirties to help them gain freedom from decisions that they made in their late teens and had controlled them throughout their twenties.

He then went on to add that more and more people within his church were now entering into their forties attempting to make up for the loss of the past twenty years by now beginning to dedicate their hearts and lives to living by God's direction and plan for their lives.

It has been said that the definition of a genius is finding someone who believes what you know to be true and yet they can articulate it simply and understandably.

In my experience, this particular pastor is a genius. And while we can rejoice at the truth of God's ability to redeem rebellious hearts and lost lives, we must equally grieve at the reality of lost time and missed opportunity.

Twenty years is a long time and provides the framework for a lot of lost opportunity.

As you stay alert be to make wise choices and trust the Words of God to build your life upon the stability of God and His promises. Avoid even the temptation of sin and keep yourself from the missed opportunity of entering into life twenty years from now with the baggage of regret from the consequences and entanglements of poor decisions in these next few years.

Fourth, I pray that you will keep innocent.

There are two types of meanings given to the word innocent throughout the pages of Scripture. The first and more prevalent is that we are to live lives apart from sin.

The second meaning is not just a definition of blamelessness but of a "lack of experience" with the bad things that happen in life. This second term is often equated with the innocence we felt when we were children before we became aware of all of the types of evil and corruption that the world offers to us.

This is the type of innocence that Adam and Eve experienced in The Garden of Eden prior to gaining the knowledge of rebellion and becoming aware of the sin that would separate them from God and each other. It was the innocence that allowed them to live without shame (Genesis 2:25, 3:7).

Modern media has a way of stealing innocence by introducing us to concepts, culture, and environments beyond the years of childhood innocence through the fantasy of images and storytelling with low-cost freedom and the opportunity to escape the false reality with relative simplicity.

But now that you are approaching the next transition in your life it is easier to gain and afford access to all types of situations, relationships, cultures and environments that will cause us to become aware of pain and pleasure in ways that we were either unaware of or had only heard about through our experience with media.

Lingering at the door
Romans 16

Choose wisely what you allow yourself to be exposed to. Paul writes to his brothers and sisters in Corinth that it is not his desire that they are childish in their understanding but that they remain innocent as babies when it comes to evil. He expands by stating that innocence does not mean immature or that they have a lack of understanding (1 Corinthians 14:20).

In other words, it is possible to be aware of evil while remaining innocent of it.

The purpose of this innocence is not merely to remain baggage free for as long as possible (although if you think about the areas in life where you wish you had stayed innocent that reason alone would most likely be enough by itself). But as Paul writes, so that we can "shine like bright lights in a world full of crooked and perverse people" (Philippians 2:15).

Our purpose for remaining innocent comes back to the concept our fulfilling our mission to reflect the glory of God in a culture that has lost sight of Him, and we cannot do that if His glory has been dulled by our involvement in the very things that we are designed to shine light upon.

When I was in the military, there were a few times when I experienced first hand the observations of others to the choices that set me apart from others. Decisions that unbeknownst to me allowed for a level of innocence that was noticeably reflected in my face to the point where they felt obliged to verbally identify and offer a compliment on their awareness of the difference.

Now, remember that innocence and immaturity are not that same. What I found shocking and what caught me off guard by the comments was the fact that they were not mocking a perceived immaturity or lack of awareness but a perceived difference that they could not quite identify a source or a reason for.

It was to me the shocking embodiment of the reality of the word of God and the truth of Philippians 2:15. Now, twenty plus years later after years of full-time Christian ministry and counseling as well as the simple reality of watching life and consequences of poor decisions rip apart the lives, marriages, and ministries of close friends there is a sense of innocence that has been lost that I would love to have back again.

A weight exists as a result of watching how the consequences of sin have ripped into and ravished the lives of people who I love. It is a weight that I carry with me now that did not exist when I was innocent of those realities.

When it comes to increasing your understanding, gain your maturity from diving deep into the pages of the revelation of God and trusting the words and admonitions that are within. When it comes to exposing yourself to evil whether through media or through choosing to directly participate, I pray that you remain innocent for as long as possible.

Fifth, I pray that you will keep pure. On some level, this admonition may seem redundant in light of the prayer to keep innocent, and while there are many similarities, there is something about purity that is worth recognizing it, as it's own prayer request.

By definition, purity contains the concept of being separate from contamination and unnecessary elements. It includes ideas that are similar to previous prayers recorded in Scripture that we are to remain innocent and untangled. But in this instance, Scripture attaches an additional thought to the concept of purity.

To be useful in the hands of the Master, a tool or resource was to be kept pure.

In his final letter to Timothy, the Apostle Paul writes that if we keep ourselves pure then we will be a special utensil used for honorable use and we will be ready for the Master to use us (2 Timothy 2:21).

Paul then follows that encouraging promise with this blunt exhortation. In light of that, Paul writes that we should "run from anything that stimulates youthful lusts and pursue righteousness, faithfulness, love and peace" (2 Timothy 2:22a).

Lingering at the door
Romans 16

Paul concludes that in our quest for purity and usefulness our choice of friendships matter when he states that we should "enjoy the companionship of those who call on the Lord with pure hearts" (2:22b).

In other words, if we desire to be pure and remain untangled to fulfill and live out the purposes and mission of God in our lives according to His best possible plan, then we need to carefully surround ourselves with likeminded companions with whom we can enjoy the journey with.

This is critical not only in our choice of friendships but ultimately in the choices we make when we choose whom to consider dating and eventually who we may consider entering into the covenant of marriage with.

Be sure that you are like-minded and that you share not only an interest but a deep and devoted passion for Christ and the value of a life built upon the solid Christ-centered yoke of His Word, His invitations and His mission.

Things to leave

In addition to the things that I pray that you keep there are also things that I pray that you leave.

First, I pray that you will leave fear and doubt behind.

As you go into "all the world" to reflect the glory of God in your new and future circles of influence, I pray that you leave your fears and your doubts behind.

By the time we reach the transition from high school to the next steps in our path to fulfilling the mission of God in our new circles of influence one of the places where the majority of us have experienced a loss of innocence is in the area of failure and defeat.

Few of us made it through our high school years unscathed from either minor or massive defeats. Whether they were experienced in the context of a relationship or in front of our peers on an athletic

field, stage or even during a classroom presentation; each of us have experienced the pain of either being cut from a team, a group of friends or just not measuring up to a preset standard that we attempted to achieve.

For some the pain was temporary, but the self-doubt still crept in.

For others, it was a valued learning experience that helped us identify an area of life where we lacked skill, talent or prowess that could be learned or acquired. For others it was not merely hurtful – it was harmful, and as a result, we carry with us fear or doubts that did not exist in our world of innocence.

I remember when my daughters were small children who loved when I would toss them up in the air and catch them. Their cries of "Again! Again!" only served to embolden us both with the increased measures of height that we were willing to risk.

At the time they experienced no fear. In their innocence, they held no concept of what it would feel like if their father dropped them. They were innocent to the idea of pain, and as a result, they looked at me with a sense of perfect trust.

Sometimes our experiences change the way we view our fathers. Sometimes our experience changes the way we view our Heavenly Father. Instead of viewing Him with childlike faith and the belief that will never experience pain, hurt, injury or disappointment we become jaded when He fails to operate at the center of our wills by not meeting our desires, demands, felts needs or expectations.

In addition, to a learned lack of trust in God, some of us have suffered a learned lack of trust in ourselves. It was not a perceived failure experienced at the hands of God that gave birth to our fear or doubt, but an actual failure or pattern of failure in our own lives that has led us to distrust ourselves.

For some of us, our failure has been simple and material. We failed to make the team, earn an award, keep a commitment, or reach a goal.

Lingering at the door
Romans 16

For others, our failure has been spiritual. We have failed to follow through on a commitment, stumbled into a familiar pattern or have become addicted to a particular sin, and with each subsequent failure, we have experienced an increase in the amount of baggage that we carry with us moving forward.

If this describes any element of your experience, then I invite you to again find comfort and empathy in the words of Paul who wrote of his own experience in his encouragement to those in Philippi.

"I don't mean to say that I have already achieved these things or that I have already reached perfection. But I press on to possess that perfection for which Christ Jesus first possessed me. 13 No, dear brothers and sisters, I have not achieved it, but I focus on this one thing: Forgetting the past and looking forward to what lies ahead, 14 I press on to reach the end of the race and receive the heavenly prize for which God, through Christ Jesus, is calling us." Philippians 3:12-14

Paul brought a ton of baggage into his relationship with Christ. He was a murderer who took the lives of men and women who he will share eternity with. But even in his growth as a Christ-follower, apostle, missionary, church planter, and pastor he admits that he still has not arrived.

He carries the baggage of personal failure and sin as well as the physical, emotional and mental scars from the beatings, betrayals, and imprisonments that he faced.

In every way, a case could be made that Paul could easily have found a quiet place where he could have distanced himself safely from God and others to nurse his wounds and attend to his fears, doubts and personal baggage.

But instead of getting caught in the past, or even attempting to make sense of every detail before moving on with his life and his mission he recognizes that it is not until we leave our baggage behind and stop looking in the rearview mirror that we can move forward and become all that God desires for us to become.

This life transition is an incredible opportunity for you to start over.

Embrace the opportunity to leave behind the baggage and reminders of the mistakes of your awkward middle school years or the stories or innuendos from who you were or decisions that you made a few years ago.

Embrace the opportunity to step into a new world and a new culture where other people have no preconceived expectations or notions about who you are, who you were or who they expect to be in their presence.

Keep the good memories. Hold steady and cultivate the cherished relationships. A bold life that acknowledges the realities of failure and disappointment also embraces the truth that the God of the Bible invites you to live boldly and to pray the prayer of Shadrach, Meshach, and Abednego, who openly proclaimed their faith in God regardless of the outcome of their decision to serve Him wholeheartedly.

"Shadrach, Meshach, and Abednego replied, "O Nebuchadnezzar, we do not need to defend ourselves before you. 17 If we are thrown into the blazing furnace, the God whom we serve is able to save us. He will rescue us from your power, Your Majesty. 18 But even if he doesn't, we want to make it clear to you, Your Majesty, that we will never serve your gods or worship the gold statue you have set up."
Daniel 3:16-18

Finally, I pray that you will leave the safety of your comfort zone.

Leaving the safety of your comfort zone and taking the types of risks with God where you will give yourself permission to make mistakes, experience failure and discover a big and grace-filled God as you learn to listen and respond to His voice is the only way that we can do anything more than just experience life.

Lingering at the door
Romans 16

Throughout the past four years, the goal of this curriculum has been to equip you to reflect Christ in your circles of influence 10 years after you graduate. The goal has never been to just ensure that you hold onto your faith, but that you will be envisioned and equipped to give it away.

Today as I am writing this in my classroom a former student stopped by and tapped on my window early this morning. He informed me that he was hosting an event today for several hundred video game enthusiasts where they would be using school property to set up giant screens and to play video games in organized competition with each other.

He then asked for prayer.

This was not merely an event organized because he enjoys video games it was an event that he and his wife had organized because they realized that without intentionality their circles of influence were typically limited to other Christians.

But this was another step in their shared process of living intentionally risky and missional lives outside of their comfort zone. They were anticipating a crowd of people with different lifestyles, value systems, and worldviews who would potentially never have a reason to hang out for a day at a Christian school and rub shoulders with a young married couple who both graduated with four-year degrees from Christian Universities.

In other words, they were stepping out of their comfort zone into an intentional circle of influence for the purpose of building relationships and reflecting Christ.

At the time of this writing, it is now a little over 14 hours and over 260 people representing multiple states later. The games are still taking place in the building next to me, and they are still live-streaming the final hours to an estimated additional 1,000 more individuals from around the world.

But so far the most significant thing about the day in the minds of this young couple is not the 1,260 people but the two people.

One person who flew in from the East Coast who is staying over at their home for the week and the other young man who just asked if he could crash at their place tonight too to attend church with them in the morning.

What makes the request cool is that there was not a sign advertising their church. Neither of them are wearing a Christian t-shirt or carrying a Bible. And they are not overtly inviting people to attend church with them in the morning.

Instead, they are simply reflecting Christ in an intentional circle of influence. And in the process, a young man who by his own admission is far from God requested the opportunity to attend their church with them in the morning.

The rest of the story is yet to be written.

Lingering at the door
Romans 16

Things to expect

The definition of equipping is to inform someone of what to expect and to give them a tool or resource to meet the expectation. In light of that, it is essential to outline a few things you should expect along in your journey to reflect Christ in your circles of influence.
First, expect warfare.

Not every story ends with a request from a random stranger to attend church with you in the morning. But step into the front lines and invite God to use you to carry out His mission and you can expect the enemy of God to be ticked off. Paul writes to the Ephesians to "put on the full armor of God" because the war is not with flesh and blood but with spiritual enemies who hate to lose ground (Ephesians 6).

Don't be surprised when you step into your circles that there is pushback. Sickness, discouragement, and conflict, are all par for the course. From experience Satan's favorite times to attack are in the early stages of a new endeavor and when you are tired but fresh off of a victory. It is during these times that we let our guard down and become vulnerable for discouragement and attack.

If you find yourself in the midst of attack be encouraged. The enemy of God believes that you are enough of a threat to make it onto his radar. Embrace the reality that few accomplishments in life that are genuinely worth anything will ever happen without a struggle.

Second, expect to have to fight the desire to become complacent.

Another of the enemy's favorite tools in the toolbox is to invite us into a false sense of victory. Perhaps you have been experiencing a level of spiritual warfare and pushback only to finally experience even a small degree of breakthrough.

It is surprising how easy it is in that moment to breathe a sigh of relief and to take your hand off the plow to enjoy a false sense of total victory or accomplishment.

The lie we believe leans toward the idea that God is lucky to have a person like us on His team. Or, the lie that the minor victory is a sign from God that we don't have to continue to press forward because things will now be easier from now on.

Both extremes typically end with us rewarding ourselves and our pride with the false accolade of our choice coupled with a later surprise that what we had experienced was not actually the top of a mountain but merely a vista on the way to the top. Sometimes the exhale of effort results spiritually in a missed opportunity or even a spiritual regression.

Third, expect times of fear and uncertainty.

There is a reason that Joshua and others throughout Scripture were reminded to fear not. Let's be honest living a life of risk that is on mission and completely dependent upon God is scary. Particularly when there are times that the only thing we can know for certain is that we are about to be or are currently in the middle of a spiritual attack. When that happens just remember that the odds are that you did not screw up. You did not mishear God. And most importantly you did not do anything wrong to cause God to punish you. Just put your head down and press forward through the power of the Holy Spirit.

Fourth, expect times of loneliness.

Years ago I was leading a team of students in a paintball battle in the middle of the woods. The game was called speedball. There was one flag positioned directly between two opposing sides approximately 50 feet apart from each other, and the goal was to run to the middle, grab the flag and then take it into the fort of the other team for the win.

Both sides had a fortified area to hide behind. Both sides were only slightly camouflaged from each other so that it was possible to see the other teams fortification before the start of the game.

Lingering at the door
Romans 16

Without some sort of cover, it was going to end up being two teams within eyesight of each other opening up full hoppers full of paintballs on each other until the last man was standing.

We were given about 5 minutes to put together a plan for the game, and I had a great plan!

My plan was to take four or five smoke grenades and toss them into the middle to provide cover and then for our entire team to scream as loud as we could as we ran through the smoke, grabbed the flagged and simply overwhelmed our surprised opponents by running the flag right up to their fort for the win.

The whistle blew to indicate the start of the game and our plan went into action.

The first few steps went off without a hitch. There was some random fire from both sides as our team pulled the pin on several smoke-grenades and created a massive cloud of cover. Once our team lined up for the bull rush, I gave the signal to start screaming. The next step was to be the entirety of our team firing our weapons and running through the smoke toward the flag.

The screaming started. The firing started, and I started to run into the smoke.

For a moment it was like one of those heroic scenes out of the movies where the military plan of action was engaged and enacted to perfection. A sense of pride swelled up inside my chest as I led our team into the battle. The smoke was thick. The screaming was loud. The pop – pop – pop –smack of the paintball markers was heard as the shots were fired off in rapid succession and the little balls smacked into targets on the other side of the smoke.

Then I exited the smoke, and through my goggles, I saw the look of terror on the faces of the opposing team. It was evident they were surprised by our tactics and that our plan was going to work to perfection. In fact, they looked so terrified that many of them were literally turning around and starting to run away.

But then as I exited out of the smoke and saw the flag just a few more steps from where I was, I realized the terror on the faces of my enemy turned to shock, and then that shock turned to a type of joy that I had never seen before nor have I seen since.

The joy expressed on their faces was summed up in the next words that I heard, "He is all alone! Get him!"

The only sound that I heard after that moment was the sound of my own voice crying out in pain coupled with the sounds of their entire team opening fire on me as I curled up I in the fetal position taking what felt like hundreds of rounds of paintballs shot from semi-automatic markers covered my body.

"I'm hit. I'm hit. I'm hit" was all that I could remember yelling!

Then as the smoke fully cleared and the opposing team walked over my bruised and battered body on to a victory over my cowardly team I heard them celebrating behind me.

Apparently, my team not only had failed to follow me through the smoke into the battle but they had failed to put up any sort of fight.

Several moments later as I finally pulled myself off the ground and had the opportunity for a team meeting to debrief the debacle before switching sides and playing a second round I could not resist asking the obvious question, "What happened?"

"Where were you?" I asked my team.

What happened?

Was this a joke?

Had they talked together and conspired to leave me alone on the other side of the smoke? And what did the other team make of what just happened? Did they pay-off my team? Was this a large-scale ruse where I was the only one who had been left out of the joke?

Lingering at the door
Romans 16

As it turned out the other team was the first to speak.

"You looked so cool coming out of that smoke," they said.

"Yeah, it was like Rambo. We were terrified," someone added.

"Until we realized that you were alone," a third student chimed in.

Although to call them teammates after this level of betrayal seems quite generous I turned to the young faces around me and said, "What happened?"

"We got scared?"

One by one each member of the team confessed that it was personal fear that had been felt in the heat of the moment and not a vast conspiracy that had led to our demise as a team and my body covered in more bruises than were possible to count.

They started screaming and saw me run into the smoke. They each were met with fear of what was on the other side of the darkness. Instead of running into the smoke toward the sound of paintballs flying in their direction, for the flag and a glorious victory, the entire team stopped dead in their tracks and waited to see what would happen.

When the smoke finally cleared the flag was on our side as the opposing team eliminated me from the completion. They had grabbed the flag and run through the smoke to claim victory while my team sat as young deer in the proverbial headlights.

To a person, each member of my team apologized to me for their act of cowardice and claimed that they had assumed that the rest of the team was going to follow me through the smoke but that they did not like the risk of getting hit, so they chose to stop.

Bottom line living life on mission with God often feels a lot like that moment; lonely.

Many will talk a good game. Some will even preach sermons or teach classes to others about what life is like when you choose to live life on mission with God yet when it comes down to the last minute, many will decide not to run into the uncertainty.

There is a moment at the end of the first chapter of Mark that describes how Jesus was forced at times into seclusion because of His ministry (1:45).

Don't be surprised if as you seek to reflect Christ in culture if there are times when you will feel a sense of loneliness.
Fifth, expect times of great pain.

In light of the real world, a body full of bruises that healed over the next few weeks made for some great talking points and even a tiny amount of sympathy from my wife. But the reality is that there are times in a life that is committed to living on mission with God where you will experience amounts of great pain.

The two keys to remember during these times is that you are not alone and that it is important that while you maintain a soft heart, it is okay to develop a thick skin.

Let me explain. First, you are not alone. Just read the bible or read a few biographies. One of the purposes for making the great cloud of witness presentations this semester was to learn to hear the similarities in the stories of the men and women who have gone before us as culture changers for the glory of God.

Each one ran through the smoke and came out on the other side only to be met with various types of great personal pain. Yet they were each commended for their faith in the face of adversity.

Lingering at the door
Romans 16

But the second key is essential in learning how to deal with the pain. It is very possible after only a short period of time for people who live on mission for Jesus Christ to develop a hard heart coupled with thin skin. In other words, the words, arrows and unfair attacks of others hurt more than we would like to let on but our heart grows hard towards the people themselves.

Typically this is a result of a desire to gain our accolades from others. We want others to see our nobility, and we care deeply about being liked, loved and appreciated by others.

In contrast, those who develop a thick skin but maintain a soft heart typically serve an audience of one. Years ago a wise mentor once connected me to the truth of Proverbs 29:25 which reads, "the fear of man will prove to be a snare, but he who trusts in the Lord is kept safe" (NIV).

This was a life-changing verse for me. As a young man, much of my twenties was squandered with the false belief that people would see and understand my heart to serve the living God and they would be happy and join not only join the mission but also join the team. Nothing could have been further from the truth.

Sure there were some very dear brothers and sisters whose hearts were united in friendship by our shared mission, but there were always others who were threatened by any hint of change in the status quo that might rock them out of their complacency.

When that happens, that threat always needs a face and a name as the result that will mean unfair and often very personal attacks on you, your character and typically on the very values that motivate you to persevere.

When that happens, and it will, I urge you to follow the advice of Dr. Warren Weirsbe who I heard speak more than twenty years ago at a conference for Pastors. Dr. Wiersbe simply said this, "Next time you are attacked without cause, just remember that even Jesus had a Judas."

Those words spoken by an individual who I admire as an incredible reflection of Christ was spoken not merely out of his own understanding of Scripture but out of his personal life experience of being betrayed by a close friend.

As a result, that lesson and the personal experience that has accompanied it throughout my own twenty years of ministry rings even more genuinely profound today than it did twenty years ago.

Sixth, expect times of confusion when those closest to you betray you.

It is a simple truth that not everyone will understand and agree with you about the path that you are on as you seek to fulfill the mission of God in your unique circle of influence.

To be blunt your decisions, your passion, your drive, and your focus will scare certain people who do not have the luxury of understanding or who are convicted because they have grown complacent over time to who God called them to become.

As a result, you will be seen as a threat to their way of life.

And as a result, there are times when you will not only find yourself running out of the smoke alone, but you may even discover that some of the shots you took were fired from behind you and you will have bruises on your back to prove it.

In the midst of your shock, pain, and exhaustion you will be tempted to turn and fire back into the ranks of those who are shooting at you from your own team. However, I would advise you that Wiersbe's insight and advice regarding a calculated response in the reflection of Christ have served me well since the day that I first hear it.

The best course of action, according to Wiersbe, was not to return fire on our attacker. Returning fire takes us from our mission and exhausts the valuable resources of time, effort and energy..

Lingering at the door
Romans 16

The best course of action is to do nothing and allow God to handle both our attacker and our reputation.

Or as Wiersbe stated, "Give Judas enough rope, and eventually he will hang himself."

The principle describes when someone is motivated to attack us with false lies and how we should respond. We have the option to stoop down into the gutter to defend ourselves.

Or if we allow God to be our defender, then eventually the truth will come out, and the lies will either get so big that they can be seen for what they are or the character of the person will become so evident that it will be seen for what it is.

Either way, our time, effort, and energy can continue to be invested in the work of the kingdom, and our trust can rest on the ability of God to watch over His sheep and our reputation.

Does it still hurt when we are attacked? Absolutely!

Is there still pain in the loneliness when those we hoped would stand with us betray us? Absolutely!

Are there moments when we want to turn and fire back because it seems like Jesus is never going to quite get around to doing it for us?

Most definitely!

But never forget Christ's silence before His accusers while He was in the midst of His phony trial before the High Priest. Eventually, after the cross, the truth about Christ would be made known, and ultimately, the truth about Judas was made known as well.

There was a moment in my life when I had a choice to fight back against a series of false accusations that were unjust. But a close friend in ministry gave me what proved to be sage counsel.
"Fight back now and you might prove yourself right in the eyes of a few people, he said, "but you will hurt other sheep in the process."

He went on to say, "Stay silent now and there will be immediate consequences for you that will be painful. But if you wait ten years and continue to live your life the way you are, and they continue to live their life the way they are then eventually you won't need to say anything because the truth will become evident to everyone. "

More than two decades later I am thankful for the council because looking back, he was right. It was painful for a season. Of that, there can be no denial. But God's grace became evident in ways that were as unimaginable as they were unexplainable.

And by His grace not only was my family persevered through the trial, but my own personal understanding of the faithfulness of God increased in ways that it never could have had I taken the battle into my own hands and defended myself.

As a result, it is not only easier to trust God, but it is easier to invite others to do the same.

Seventh, expect that some people just will not understand.

There was a time in my early days of ministry when what could only be defined as a revival swept through the lives of our students. Junior and Senior High school students were being made right with God and seeking Him not only for their own personal transformation but also for the salvation and transformation of their circles of influence in their schools.

At one point in the process, we were seeing students praying for students, and it was not unusual for unsaved students to invite their unsaved friends to prayer meetings only to end up hearing the gospel and receiving Christ for themselves.

Yet not everyone thought that this was an amazing God thing. Some within our church were concerned as they put it, "that students were becoming too heavenly minded for any earthly good" and that "students should be doing less praying at church and playing more youth group games."

Lingering at the door
Romans 16

I confess, that in the midst of the students who were receiving Christ and needing to be discipled that there was not a lot of time for games during our 90 minutes of weekly student ministry during that season.

In fact, at one point I opened up an evening by asking if anyone wanted to go into the gym and play a game and one of the first time students shouted out, "Wait, I thought this was the church where people prayed? I came here because I need someone to pray for me, not to go play a game!"

Multiple similar moments coupled with my youthful vigor and naiveté led me to operate under the false assumption that the problem with our naysayers was that they did not understand what was taking place because they had not seen it first hand.

I also operated under the false assumption that if they merely attended one of our 90 minute evenings, they would soon share our conclusion.

They would see that game time was not needed by the students. They were too busy praying for each other and being equipped to understand and apply the Bible to their lives.

I was wrong on both assumptions.

After accepting my invitation to attend an evening and seeing first hand the amazing things that God was doing in and through the lives of students who were being used by God to reach their peers and reflect Christ in their circles of influence it only seemed to embolden our naysayers instead of silence them.

The truth is that Jesus experienced the same set of reactions from the religious folks in His day. It was not that they could not see the evidence of physical healing and life transformation in front of their eyes it was that those were not the results that they wanted.

The reality was that the Pharisees and other religious leaders preferred the charade of religious activity to the reality of transformed lives.

The same is sometimes true in our culture when Jesus shows up and begins to upset the status quo by changing lives.

The key is not to get upset or be surprised. In fact, the truth is that there really is nothing that you and I can do to change a heart. The Bible is clear that it is the Spirit and power of God alone that changes hearts. It is our job to sow the seed and then run with the runners.

Jesus taught this principle when he sent out his disciples as "sheep among wolves" in a culture that had yet to hear the good news of the rabbi. In Luke 10:6, Jesus instructs His disciples to seek out the "man of peace."

Peace is one of the fruits of the Spirit. Jesus was sending the people to with the instruction that the Spirit of God was already at work in the hearts of certain individuals.

Look for the man of peace, and you will discover those whose hearts the Holy Spirit has prepared. Find those whose heart the Spirit of God has made ready, and you will find those who are ready to run. Run with the runners, and you will run and not grow weary. But attempt to do the work of the Holy Spirit and change a heart that is hardened toward the invitations of Christ and the work of the Spirit, and you will find yourself fighting against a religious spirit and spinning your wheels in exhaustion.

Final thoughts

In a paraphrased oversimplification of the words of Winston Churchill - don't give up.

Expect that through everything God will show up and reveal himself to you in ways that you never imagined.

Each of us has a limited number of hours, days and years on this earth. Remember that Jesus died so that you could live. Go into "all the world" and make the most of your opportunity to become the reflection that God desires you to become and to discover the circle where God designed for you to thrive. Blessings on your journey!

Where is my modern Jerusalem, Greece & Rome?
Socratic Dialogue

Part II. Class Notes and Discussion

Jerusalem, Greece & Rome Project & Presentation

History repeats itself if nobody listens

Facing the Giants in the valley of our modern Elah

Part I.

> Students will make a formal researched presentation on a modern-day cultural giant and provide analysis, interpretation, and understanding of the current tension between Culture & Theology along with a proposal for an integrated Christ-centered solution.
>
> Student presentations will include a handcrafted visual aid but may not include a power point, keynote or slide deck presentation.
>
> Students will submit a formal single page reflection detailing the cultural giant that then have researched demonstrating rigorous academic interaction with the following questions.
>
> The student presentation will be 4-7 minutes long. Academic research and personal reflection to the seven questions that displaying an understanding of the principles taught in this course must be evident through oral or visual communication during the presentation.

Part II. Questions for research and reflection

1. What was the cultural giant that our generation is facing?

    - Why is it a giant?
    - How is it holding back the mission of God on the earth?
    - Why should we care?
    - Why does this demand a solution?

2. What is the Christ-centered solution that you are proposing?

3. What would be the cultural pressure that would be faced if your solution was implemented?
4. What opposition should be expected?

5. What events or circumstances in your life has God or would God need to use to prepare you to face the giant?

6. Of the five perspectives; what approach toward Christ and culture which one are you opting for?

7. What are some other attempts that people are making to try to remove this giant? What perspective toward Christ and culture are they utilizing?

8. Who would be a heroic "witness" from the past that you could learn from and apply lessons from their life or approach toward your solution?

Jerusalem, Greece & Rome Project & Presentation
"The only thing necessary for the triumph of evil is for good men to do nothing"
- Edmund Burke

What are some of the modern giants standing in valley of our culture?

What would be a Christ-centered approach to…

1	Apathetic Church	26	Human Cloning
2	Lack of Discipleship	27	Genetic Engineering
3	Church Planting	28	Euthanasia and the value of human life
4	Modern Missions	29	Stem Cell Research
5	The redefining of marriage	30	"Going Green" and the environment
6	The redefining of gender	31	Modern Ecumenicalism
7	The redefining of faith	32	Global Poverty (or country specific)
8	The redefining of the atonement	33	Localized Poverty
9	Issues facing the South American Church	34	Orphans
10	Issues facing the Latin American Church	35	Child Abuse
11	Issues facing the Asian Church	36	Domestic Violence
12	Issues facing the European Church	37	Addition
13	Issues facing the Church in England	38	Human Slavery (trafficking)
14	The future of evangelism in a postmodern generation	39	Welfare
15	The future of evangelism in an internet generation	40	Joblessness
16	Modern praise and worship	41	The New Age Movement
17	Fair trade	42	Modern Gnosticism in the church
18	The debt of nations	43	Anti-Semitism
19	The debt of the average family	44	The State of Israel
20	War	45	The persecuted church
21	Terrorism	46	The rise of Islam
22	Immigration	47	The rise of Mormonism
23	Modern Youth Ministry	48	International Christian Education
24	The tension between faith and science	49	Bible Teacher Training for Secondary Ed
25	New Atheism	50	Other? Don't see something on the list… make a proposal.

Jerusalem, Greece and Rome Presentations

"The only thing necessary for the triumph of evil is for good men to do nothing"
- Edmund Burke

Jerusalem, Greece and Rome Presentations

"The only thing necessary for the triumph of evil is for good men to do nothing"
- Edmund Burke